The kiss
passionatel

'You're sure y̶o̶[...] asked softly. He was all too well aware of the effect his lovemaking had produced. Colt was playing with Jessica, amusing himself at her expense. No doubt it was something of a novelty to have to try and persuade a woman into his bed.

Well, he could look elsewhere for his diversions. 'I want more than a performance in bed. Trust, faithfulness—love; I prefer those things.'

'And that was what your fiancé gave you, was it, while he was sleeping with your sister?'

Helen Brooks lives in Northamptonshire and is married with three children. As she is a committed Christian, busy housewife and mother, her spare time is at a premium, but her hobbies include reading, swimming, gardening and walking her two energetic, inquisitive and very endearing young dogs. Her long-cherished aspiration to write became a reality when she put pen to paper on reaching the age of forty, and sent the result off to Mills & Boon.

Recent titles by the same author:

RECKLESS FLIRTATION
THE PRICE OF A WIFE
HUSBAND BY CONTRACT
SECOND MARRIAGE

SATISFACTION GUARANTEED

BY
HELEN BROOKS

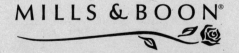

MILLS & BOON®

MILLS & BOON and MILLS & BOON with the Rose Device are registered trademarks of the publisher.

First published in Great Britain 1997
Harlequin Mills & Boon Limited,
Eton House, 18-24 Paradise Road, Richmond, Surrey TW9 1SR

© Helen Brooks 1997

ISBN 0 263 80403 8

Set in Times Roman 10½ on 10¾ pt.
01-9710-60000 C1

Printed and bound in Great Britain
by Mackays of Chatham PLC, Chatham

CHAPTER ONE

'I HAVE to say I wish I'd never let you talk me into this, Carol.' Jessica slanted her deep brown eyes at her cousin, adjusting her position on the uncomfortable wooden bench with a little wriggle. 'It's got all the makings of a first-class disaster, and I've got the niggly feeling that's exactly what it's going to be.'

'Don't be such a grouch; it doesn't suit you.' Carol smiled sunnily at the beautiful face frowning so ferociously in her direction. 'Think of all the lovely money we're going to make this afternoon.'

'Blow the money.' Jessica's scowl deepened.

'*Jess…*'

'I mean it, Carol. If you're so enthusiastic about the idea, why can't you do it? At least you know everyone.'

'Exactly.' Carol grimaced, an action that caused her gentle blue eyes to disappear into the plump cheeks beneath them. 'I'm not exactly a new point of interest, now, am I? Besides which, can you see any man beating a path to my door? Whereas you…' She let her eyes sweep over her cousin's flawless complexion, shoulder-length ash-blonde hair and large dark eyes set in a skin that was truly peaches and cream. 'You're something else.'

'You're as good as me any day. I wish you wouldn't run yourself down the way you do.' Jessica's face had mellowed along with her voice. 'Robbie thinks you're gorgeous, anyway.'

'Maybe.' The shadow that passed over Carol's round face wasn't lost on Jessica, and she determined to have a good chat with her later once the fête had finished. She had felt there was something wrong from the moment

she had stepped off the train earlier that day, but Carol
never had been one for wearing her heart on her sleeve.
But if that doctor of hers was giving her any trouble…
The frown took hold again. He'd have Jessica to answer
to; he really would. Carol was a darling—everyone knew
that—and he was dead lucky to have her.

'Anyway, think of the church roof and the thousands
the repairs are going to cost,' Carol added quietly.

'Carol, I couldn't give a monkey's about the church
roof.' Jessica sighed patiently. 'I'm doing this for you,
and you only, although I'm still not really sure how I
let you talk me into it. The tombola I wouldn't have
minded, the cake stall—even the coconut shy I could
have coped with quite happily. But selling kisses at a
pound a kiss? I'm not sure which will be worse—if there
are no takers at all and I sit here like a lemon, or if all
the fellas feel duty bound to have a pound's worth.
Either way it's embarrassing. And that banner…' She
glared at the gaily decorated strip of cloth hanging
straight above the bench. 'Whose bright idea was that?'

'Mine.' Carol grinned wickedly. 'Don't you like it,
then?'

'*Like it?*' Jessica shut her eyes, shaking her head wearily. 'I don't know how you're on such good terms with
the vicar, I really don't, unless you give him plenty to
pray about, that is.'

'I think it's brilliant.' Carol was openly laughing now.
'"Satisfaction Guaranteed"—that should interest even
the most staid members of our community, don't you
think?'

'Just make sure you stick pretty close,' Jessica demanded, although the severity of her tone was spoilt
somewhat by the smile she couldn't hide. 'In case some
of that interest you mention proves troublesome.'

'In Brindale?' Carol scoffed disparagingly. 'You must
be joking, Jess. This is the original little backwater, as
well you know, with everyone related to everyone else.
No one would dream of making a pass at you. I wouldn't

have asked you to do this if I thought any different. I know you London career women have to watch your backs—and possibly your fronts—all the time but life is different down here. Slower, friendlier.'

'Carol, men are men the world over.' Jessica wasn't smiling now. 'As well I know. And I repeat, you stay close.'

'All right, all right.' Carol nodded hastily, mentally kicking herself for being so indiscreet. She still couldn't believe that William and Jo—*Jo* of all people—had let Jess down so badly, and now she'd gone and reminded her cousin of the fact. And when she was down here doing her a favour as well. Oh, she'd got a big mouth; she really had. 'I'll be your second skin.'

'Hovering at my shoulder will do.' The smile was back as Jessica absorbed Carol's woebegone expression. 'And don't look so tragic; I'm over William now. He did me a favour, really. Taught me a lesson I'll never forget.'

Carol would have felt more reassured if Jessica had mentioned Jo too, and now she bit her lip before saying, 'Oh, Jess, don't let it spoil things for you.'

'He hasn't.' There was a forced brightness to Jessica's voice that spoke volumes. 'I told you, I'm over him.'

'I didn't mean that, I meant—'

But what Carol meant was never voiced as the loudspeaker at the other end of the school playing field where the fête was being held suddenly blared into life, announcing that the gate was to be opened and the fête could commence.

'Here we go.' Carol pulled a face at Jessica before standing slowly and smoothing her dress over sturdy thighs. 'They'll make straight for the ''nearly new'' stall; they always do. And the toy one; that's always a big favourite. We had two young mums practically fighting last year over a box of He-Man figures—the vicar had to act as arbitrator in the end.'

'Did he?' Jessica giggled at the picture Carol's words

had conjured up. 'What about this stall? Have you ever had any problems with this?'

'No one's done this before.' Carol realised too late that she shouldn't have admitted to this fact as Jessica's horrified *'Carol!'* caused several women, who were hurrying by armed with stout shopping bags, to glance in their direction before they continued their launch towards the 'nearly new' stall a few yards away.

'What do you mean, no one's done it before?' Jessica growled as Carol stepped dutifully behind her. But then the first customer—a small round barrel of a man with an equally small round barrel of a wife—appeared in front of her, gave her a peck on the cheek along with a generous contribution to the church fund and, smiling, disappeared into the crowd, his wife nodding at her as they went.

'See?' Carol's voice expressed great satisfaction along with an element of relief she couldn't hide. 'I told you it would be all right, didn't I? This isn't London, Jess; people are so much more polite here. No one will take advantage. It just isn't done.'

And the next hour seemed to prove Carol right. Young, not so young and plain elderly men all took their turn, wives and girlfriends on their arms, for a restrained peck on the cheek as the amount of money for the church fund mounted.

The sky was a bright, cloudless blue, the air soft and warm and scented with the heady perfume of countless flowers from the surrounding village gardens. With the sun caressing her face and the knowledge that she was helping a worthwhile cause to prosper, Jessica found she was actually beginning to enjoy herself. The whole environment was so different from the busy tempo of her normal life as personal assistant to an up-and-coming marketing executive who fancied himself a millionaire before he reached the age of forty. This atmosphere was relaxed, easy, villagey... So when the thunderbolt hit, just an hour and fifteen minutes after the fête had started, she couldn't have been less prepared.

'Now there's a promise you don't see every day.' The deep, slightly husky voice brought Jessica's head springing round from watching Carol, well across the other side of the field, carefully picking her way amongst hordes of excited children with a loaded tray in her hand. They had decided to treat themselves to cream cakes and iced lemonade courtesy of the school kitchen, which was doing a roaring trade as the afternoon got hotter and hotter.

She felt the jolt her heart made as she found herself staring up into a pair of keen grey eyes, but, mercifully, years of living and working in the big city where thoughts and emotions were best kept under wraps prevented her face from revealing the momentary panic. She had seen grey eyes before—dove-grey, dusky grey, grey with the soft suggestion of a hint of colour—blue or hazel. But these eyes were almost charcoal, with the hardness of slate—dark and compelling like one of the larger birds of prey.

'I...' She should have had a light, witty answer ready for what was, after all, nothing more than a social pleasantry on a warm June afternoon in the country. But she found her power of speech was not as easily controlled as her expression. 'It...it's not a promise.'

'No?' He raised his eyes to the banner again, giving her a moment to take in the whole of him. And what a whole, she thought as her heart continued to flutter in tiny palpitating gasps. The long, lean masculine body clothed intimidatingly in black denims and a black silk shirt was arresting enough, but his face... The heavily lashed grey eyes that had held her with such piercing intensity were set in a cruel, firm-lipped face that was both sensual and harsh. The cheekbones were high and beautifully sculpted and his nose was aquiline, adding to the impression of predatory power. His hair was black—jet-black, without a hint of colour—and he wore it long

into the nape of his neck, brushed back from his forehead with a careless disregard for fashion that spoke
volumes about the man himself.

Never one for instant judgements—having found too
often in the past that they were invariably proved
wrong—she nevertheless knew she didn't like him. More
than that—he frightened her.

'What, then?' The grey eyes sliced into her again with
all the softness of honed steel. 'If not a promise, how
would you describe it? A statement? An…incitement?'
There was the merest pause before the last word made
it clear how he, at least, viewed the banner, and right at
that moment Jessica could have cheerfully strangled
Carol for putting her in such a ridiculous position. Then,
in the next instant as he nonchalantly tossed a twenty-
pound note into the tub at the side of her, the full enormity of that position washed over her. He wasn't going
to kiss her…was he?

'I…I wouldn't describe it as anything,' she gabbled
frantically, quite unaware of the now all too obvious
alarm in her face and body language. 'This…this is just
a fête, for the church roof.'

'Ah, the church roof.' There was a shadow of wicked
amusement in the husky voice that told her he had
sensed her nervousness and was thoroughly enjoying it.
And that, more than anything else, brought her chin up,
her body stiffening at his unspoken challenge.

She was vaguely aware of Carol arriving at her side
clutching the tray, and of the other man standing just
beside her tormentor, but she kept her eyes fixed on him
as she said, 'Can I take it you've just bought a kiss?'

'Indeed you can.' His eyes dropped to her lips and
she was mortifyingly aware that her colour matched the
vivid pink of Carol's dress, but she dutifully rose from
the bench as he took a step forward and the next moment
she was in his arms.

She hadn't expected a timid peck on the cheek—he
was as unlike the rest of the men at the fête as the pro-

verbial wolf among a flock of sheep, after all. No, she had expected something more in the way of a macho statement of his prowess in the sex stakes, which she would have to endure as stoically as she could. So when she was gently enfolded into the hard planes of his body, and his mouth brushed hers in a tantalising, teasing shadow of a kiss—which was as unlike the expected clumsy wet assault as it was possible for it to be—her eyes opened wide with surprise.

'Shut your eyes.' Unforgivable amusement was all too evident in the dryness of his voice as he raised his head from hers.

'What?' She hated the breathless note in her voice.

'I said, shut your eyes,' he repeated patiently.

'Why?' He was still holding her but she made no effort to move away, partly because she wasn't sure her legs would hold her up. In the last few seconds the expensive, sensual smell of him had wrapped itself round her and she was horrified at what it was doing to her libido, the flickers of desire that were snaking down her limbs both intrusive and unwelcome.

'Because we've another nineteen kisses to go, that's why,' he said quietly, his voice deceptively mild.

'You don't mean...you aren't going to...? I thought you'd made a donation...' She wasn't making sense but he seemed to understand her horrified whisper.

'I did.' The slate eyes narrowed, the black lashes far too gorgeous for a man at these close quarters. 'But I haven't got to where I am today without expecting value for money, Miss...?'

'Taylor—Jessica Taylor.' He wasn't going to shake her hand now, was he? she thought, with a touch of hysteria.

'Well, Miss Jessica Taylor, I've sampled the goods and I like them. I like them very much. So when you're ready...?'

Fighting back an excitement that was as thrilling as it was shameful, she said as coldly as she could, 'Most men were content with one kiss, in view of the cause it's for.'

'I'm not most men.'

Say something, Carol—*do* something, Jessica thought helplessly. But out of the corner of her eye she was aware that the other man had engaged her cousin in conversation, and realised she could expect no help from Carol, who was now standing with her back towards them.

This time the kiss seemed to go on for ever, and through the desire and sheer pleasure of it she was conscious of thinking, somewhere in the far recesses of her mind, that the sort of finesse he was displaying didn't come without some heavy experience. He was good—far, far too good—and it made a nonsense of her earlier notion that he was out to prove something. He didn't need to prove anything to anyone, and she suspected he knew that only too well.

In fact, all things considered, he took the word arrogant to a new dimension. But oh—her toes curled and her hands tightened on the broad, hard shoulders—he could kiss. She couldn't remember feeling like this in her life—and now it was happening in the middle of a noisy fête on a hot June afternoon! That was when the alarm signals went off, loud and fierce, in her mind, and she jerked away from him as though he had burnt her.

'That's enough.' Her voice was a thick whisper but he heard it.

'Perhaps you're right.' As her eyes focused dazedly on his face she saw a small, rueful smile twisting the cruel mouth. 'Perhaps I *had* better consider the cause after all. It wouldn't do to shock the vicar, or all these good country folk, would it? But you really ought to take that thing above your head down, Miss Jessica Taylor.' Her name was drawled mockingly and in such a way that her flesh burnt hotter. 'I'm not sure if it's libellous or slanderous or what, but it sure as hell is wrong. I've never felt less satisfied in my life. In fact the only thing that would help right now is a long, cold shower.'

'That's hardly my fault, is it?' she bit out tightly as scalding embarrassment made her want to sink through the floor.

'Well, I didn't do it all by myself, if that's what you mean.'

'You know what I mean,' she retorted quietly, vitally aware of the other two who were still talking animatedly on the perimeter of her vision. 'You're supposed to just have a kiss on the cheek, something like that, not…not maul me.'

'Maul you?' The dark eyes were very intent on her face. 'I hardly kissed you, Miss Taylor, let alone mauled you. And why the sudden hostility?'

'Hardly kissed me?' She ignored his other words because she didn't dare consider them. 'Oh, come on—'

'No, you come on.' He moved very close again, looking down at her from a height which dwarfed her own five feet eight by at least six inches. 'You think that was in any way a kiss, a real kiss?' he asked softly. 'Do you? Because if so I can see your education in certain areas has been sadly mishandled. When I kiss you, my prickly little country girl—*really* kiss you—you won't move away from me, I can promise you that. And next time it won't be on a school playing field in the middle of coconut shies and small children with ice creams and dirty noses, but somewhere altogether more…conducive.'

'Next time?' She raised her head proudly, furious at the veiled accusation that she was a country bumpkin unused to handling the attention of a male. How dared he? How *dared* he act as though she was just waiting to be noticed by him? 'And what makes you think there is going to be a next time?'

'Trust me.' He smiled but his eyes remained untouched by any humour, the dangerous indolence in his voice warning her that he meant what he said.

'I somehow think that would be a very foolish thing to do,' she said as calmly as she could. 'Almost as foolish as thinking that there is any likelihood we will meet again.'

'Why are you fighting me, Jessica?' he asked softly.

'Fighting you?' She forced a laugh that was supposed to sound contemptuous but merely sounded feeble. 'I don't know you, for goodness' sake. Just because I objected to being manhandled—'

'I'll ignore that.' His eyes never left hers as he spoke, their darkness chilling and his mouth cynical as he continued with an abruptness that surprised her, 'Goodbye, Jessica Taylor.'

And then he was gone, striding into the crowd like a great black stallion, as different from the villagers in their gaily coloured summer clothes as a man-eating shark was from pretty little coral fish. She saw the pleasant, slightly rotund man who was with him nod quickly to Carol before diving off himself. But all she could do was sink down onto the bench with her hands to her flushed cheeks, her legs finally giving way.

'Wow. Oh, wow...' Carol was still gazing after the two men as she edged to Jessica's side. 'Do you know who that was?'

'Who? The one who kissed me or the one you couldn't take your eyes off?' Jessica asked weakly, and then immediately regretted the tone as Carol's eyes swung down to her face, their blue depths suddenly intuitive.

'Do I detect an element of "maiden overcome"?' Carol drawled interestedly, her gaze taking in Jessica's pink cheeks and dazed eyes.

'No, you do not!' The fierceness was out of proportion to the question and caused Carol's face to brighten still more.

'You do—you fancy him, don't you?' she persisted, joining Jessica on the bench before handing her a cream cake.

'*Carol.*'

'All right, all right.' Carol spoke through a mouthful of cream bun as she waved her free hand in a placatory gesture. 'It is allowed, you know—fancying the male sex. And you certainly wouldn't be the first to fall for Colt Irons.'

'Colt Irons? Who…?' And then the penny dropped, and with it Jessica's jaw. 'He's not… You aren't telling me he's the shipping magnate who's been in the news recently? Not *that* Colt Irons?'

'The very same.' Carol glanced at the plate Jessica was still holding in her hand. 'Do you want that cake? 'Cos I'm absolutely starving…'

'Here.' Jessica thrust the plate into her cousin's hand. 'But if that's Colt Irons, what on earth is he doing in Brindale of all places? And here? At this fête? Someone's having you on, Carol.'

'Not at all.' Carol grinned at her cheerfully as she finished her first bite of the second bun. 'Did you see the man I was talking to? That's Lord Brindale's youngest son, Harry. I've met him once or twice round and about since he finished at university.' Her cousin's cheeks turned slightly pink and now it was Jessica's turn to look interested. 'And, apparently, Colt Irons is down for a weekend in the country at their estate.'

Jessica nodded without speaking. She had seen the Brindales' castle-like manor house from a distance through the massive wrought-iron gate, from which the main drive and gardens could also be viewed. Carol had told her that the estate in whole stretched for some hundreds of acres, and she knew that the Brindale family owned practically the whole village and lots of land thereabouts.

'Apparently they were playing tennis earlier and one of the servants mentioned they were leaving early to attend the fête, and Colt thought it might be fun to pass by.'

'To see how the yokels live?' Jessica suggested sourly.

'Probably,' Carol agreed without a shred of rancour. 'He's been working hard the last few months over that deal that's been in the press so much, so perhaps he thought a complete change of scene would be restful.'

'Poor him.' Jessica narrowed her eyes. 'All those millions and millions of pounds he's got must weigh terribly heavy on the poor soul.'

'I thought you liked him?' Carol queried now as Jessica's tone finally got through.

'Well, you thought wrong.' Jessica reached down to the tray at her feet and took a long gulp of iced lemonade. 'He's the most egotistical, arrogant, bumptious man I've met in a long, long time—and I meet quite a few in the city, I might add.'

'Oh.' Carol looked more than a little put out. 'You seemed to be getting on all right with him.'

'Carol, he bought a kiss, that's all—and was pretty obnoxious into the bargain, if you want to know. If I never see him again in the whole of my life it'll suit me just fine.'

'Right.' Silence reigned while Carol finished the cake and then she asked tentatively with her eyes on the plate, 'So if I said I'd accepted an invitation for both of us to a party at the manor house tonight you wouldn't be particularly pleased?'

'You haven't!'

'I have.' Carol turned to her imploringly. 'Please, Jess, come with me. I didn't know you didn't like Colt Irons, but this is the first time Harry's asked me...' Her voice trailed away as Jessica stared at her in amazement.

'But what about Robbie?' she asked slowly, the sensation that she was fast losing her grasp on reality getting stronger. 'Won't he mind?'

'He's dating his receptionist.' The words were bleak and painful. 'With all that you've been through recently I didn't want to mention it.'

'Oh, Carol.' Jessica stared at her cousin, aghast.

'I know.' Carol gulped deep in her throat and then forced a brave smile. 'But it's not as if—' She stopped abruptly and then blushed scarlet as she realised what she had been about to say. 'I mean…'

'It's not as if you were left at the altar?' Jessica said stonily.

'Oh, Jess.' Carol's voice was anguished.

'Well, it's true, isn't it? Perhaps we ought to discuss it instead of skirting round the issue every time we meet. William left me at the altar, literally—so no, I don't suppose Robbie finding someone else is quite as bad as that humiliation. But you loved him and I loved William so that makes us equal heart-wise. Are you over him?' She turned to her cousin and looked her full in the face.

'No.' Carol gave a little sob as she spoke.

'I see.' Oh, hell, she didn't need this; she really didn't. Jessica knew a moment of deep remorse as the thought sprang into her mind but she couldn't deny it. She was just about dragging herself out of the black pit she had been thrown into five months ago, although there were still days when she wished she had never been born. And she was still hurting too badly to be of much use to anyone else.

Nevertheless, she drew her cousin into her arms and gave her a big hug as the fête went on around them, her eyes sparking fire as she wished Robert Stanton into a place where it was very hot and very final.

And so it was that, late that evening, Jessica found herself getting ready for a party she had no desire to attend and wishing with all her heart that she had stayed closeted in her little bedsit in London for the weekend.

She wasn't even *dressed* for a party, she thought savagely as she stared at her reflection in the narrow full-length mirror in her aunt's spare room, her eyes stormy and ebony-dark, throwing the pale contrast of her hair and creamy skin into even more striking relief. She had

brought clothes for a casual weekend in the country—
although her baggy white linen trousers, when teamed
with the scarlet silk shirt Carol had lent her, would just
about do. The shirt was two sizes too big but the style
was such that it didn't really matter, as she was wearing
it open with a sleeveless white top underneath.

'What am I doing…?' She stopped in the task of fixing her hair high on her head, a few long, soft, curling
tendrils falling down about the slender line of her neck,
and sank onto the bed with a little sigh. She had never
felt less like meeting a crowd of strangers in her life. Up
to five months ago a surprise evening out like this would
have been anticipated with unconcealed glee, but she
wasn't the same woman she had been then…

She shut her eyes tightly, the rushing sensation of
blind panic she had felt on that January afternoon threat-
ening to overwhelm her again. How many times had
they driven the circuit of the church? Five, six? It had
seemed like six hundred. The interested crowd of on-
lookers outside, sensing the heady smell of juicy scandal
like bloodhounds after a fox, had peered in the window
at her each time she'd arrived back at the church and
her father, bless him, had been getting angrier and angrier as his concern for her grew.

She still had moments of thinking it must all be a bad
dream, in the first few seconds of waking in the morning,
although her mind was fooling her less and less now as
her subconscious accepted the truth it had fought against
for months. William had betrayed her, humiliated her in
the worst possible way—and with Jo…

'Don't think about them.' She spoke out loud,
springing to her feet and attacking her hair with renewed
vigour. She had meant what she'd said to Carol earlier:
she *had* learnt a valuable lesson in the school of life,
and one which was indelibly printed on her very soul.
She had gone to her wedding happily, confident in her
future and their shared love. She would have trusted
William with her life without a second thought. And

now she would never be so foolish as to trust any man again...

Her train of thought suddenly brought Colt Irons' dark, sardonic face onto the screen of her mind and she flinched visibly at the knowledge he would be there tonight. She could just imagine the mocking, patronising satisfaction he would get from her presence when she had insisted, so vehemently, that they wouldn't meet again. Well, the fête was over and she didn't have any reason to suffer his particular brand of male arrogance tonight—if he even deigned to notice her, of course.

Colt Irons... Thirty-five years old, if the newspapers were to be believed, entrepreneur extraordinaire, shipping magnate, self-made and by all accounts ruthless tycoon; the list was endless. As were his women. Her mouth thinned as she remembered the tea-time conversation with Carol and her parents, when her uncle had related his tabloid knowledge of Colt Irons' love life, warning them to steer well clear of the man.

Not that he need have bothered, she acknowledged silently. It was clear that Carol's interest lay in the direction of Lord Brindale's youngest son, which was worrying in itself when she considered Carol's patent vulnerability in view of the abrupt end to her two-year association with Robert Stanton. And as for herself... She had made up her mind over the last few months, as she had clawed her way out of the abyss of bitter hurt and despair, that, for the next few years at least, she would concentrate solely and wholly on her career.

Her nomadic childhood, due to her father's job as a marine biologist, had been followed by a good university education. Hard work had ensured a first-class degree in business studies, backed by a proficiency in French and German with a smattering of several other languages besides. She was twenty-four years old and merely at the start of life, she told herself, reaching for her make-up and applying a smudge of eyeshadow to her eyelids. Already she had a job she thoroughly enjoyed, with the chance to travel and see even more of the world. She wouldn't necessarily have chosen the path she now seemed destined to tread—she forced her mind away from the slightly negative thought—but she would enjoy herself—she *would*. Work hard, play hard…

But what about the beautiful mock-Georgian family house she and William had bought, with its large tree-filled garden and vegetable patch where she had dreamt of putting down roots at long last, having a family, being a wife and mother…?

'Stop it right now,' she told herself firmly as her heart lurched and thudded painfully on. The house was sold; that dream was finished, over. There was no going back. And she was thinking too much today, which always left her drained and desolate. She *knew* that did no good. It was his fault—Colt Irons'. He had got under her skin somehow and she didn't like it. And she liked *him* still less.

Her eyes narrowed as she surveyed the slender, ethereal reflection in front of her, although her gaze acknowledged none of the beauty evident in her face and figure. If he *did* notice her tonight, and subjected her to more of his clever talking and patronising brand of arrogance, then she would make it clear exactly what she thought of him. She would.

She took a deep pull of air, nodding her head at the woman in the mirror, who nodded back with serious intent. She was her own person now—she would not be talked down to or fed some worn chat-up lines or made to feel inferior. And she would never, *ever* be lied to again. That above all else.

CHAPTER TWO

'MISS JESSICA TAYLOR…' The deep voice with its husky overtones sounded just behind her left shoulder as she stood with Carol, glass in hand, under an exquisite chandelier in the massive baronial hall at Brindale House.

They had arrived by taxi just a few minutes earlier to find the house and grounds alive with people, an extremely polite but well-muscled gateman only allowing the taxi onto the drive after he had checked their names on an invitation list that seemed to stretch to the floor.

'Well, at least this Harry friend of yours had the sense to add our names to the scroll,' Jessica had whispered to Carol as they'd nodded graciously at the now smiling attendant. 'I thought for an awful moment we were going to be sent home with our tails between our legs.'

After the taxi had deposited them at the foot of the wide circular steps leading to the studded oak door, one of several uniformed waiters had ushered them into the interior of the house and, after providing them with a glass of champagne, had disappeared into the general throng. Harry had appeared almost immediately at Carol's side. 'I'm so glad you could come.'

Jessica had watched her cousin turn pink, and had just opened her mouth to alleviate what had become a charged moment when that hateful drawl had stopped her breath.

She now purposely waited for a full ten seconds before turning slowly, forcing her mouth into a cool social smile that almost faltered as she met the mocking grey gaze of Colt Irons. 'I had no idea we would renew our acquaintance so soon, Miss Taylor.' He smiled and her nerve-endings exploded. 'Perhaps I had better introduce myself. Colt Irons, at your service.'

She doubted if he would be at anyone's service, ever. He was born to lead, not to serve. The stupid thought hit her from nowhere and did nothing to soften her expression as she inclined her head at him. 'How do you do?' The wicked glint in the devastating black-lashed eyes told her he was well aware of her animosity. Aware of it—and perhaps even relishing it?

'I do remarkably well, Miss Taylor.' He did—oh, he did, she thought agitatedly. The tall, muscled body was even more compelling in the formal evening clothes in which he was attired. 'And I had that cold shower,' he continued with a wry lift of his black eyebrows. 'Two, as a matter of fact.'

'Really?' The word carried a wealth of polite boredom and his lips twitched in appreciation.

'Yes, really.' There was cynicism in the curve of that cruel mouth but his voice was soft as he said, 'I haven't had to do that in a very, very long time.'

'I'm sorry, Mr Irons, but what makes you think that your…bathing habits are of any interest whatsoever to me?' she asked quietly, keeping her expression under strict control. It was an original approach, she had to give him that, but then if half of what her uncle had said was true he had perfected his technique many years ago. And he might as well know right now that this was one potential conquest that had not the slightest possibility of fruition.

'Jessica, Jessica…' His voice was mockingly reproachful, but at least he had dropped the 'Miss Taylor' that had grated on her nerves like barbed wire, she thought tightly. 'What a prickly wench you are, to be sure.'

'Now just you look here—'

'Colt, *sweetheart*, I can't believe my eyes—is it really you?'

Jessica saw the expression on his face freeze over as

the affected female voice behind him cut into their conversation. And, on the premise that such moments were heaven-sent, she moved gracefully to one side, seizing Carol's arm as she did so and whisking her away from a surprised Harry Brindale before either of them had a chance to speak.

'Jessica!' Carol's voice was mortified. 'What on earth are you doing? That was so rude!'

'I know.' She continued her march into the crowded drawing room as she spoke, her voice penitent. 'And I'm sorry, I'm really sorry, Carol. But you'll have a chance to speak to Harry again and I had to get away from that hateful man. He's...he's just past belief.'

'Colt Irons?' Carol glanced back over her shoulder. 'Yes, he is rather amazing, isn't he?' she agreed with some relish.

'I didn't mean it like that, and you know it.' They stopped for breath beside two middle-aged women who were so festooned with jewels they resembled brightly lit Christmas trees.

'Oh, I know, Jess. Really.' Carol put out her hand and touched Jessica's arm, her face concerned. 'But perhaps...perhaps someone like Colt Irons is what you need right now—a light flirtation for the evening that can't possibly go anywhere but will make you feel good.'

'Make me feel good?' Jessica stared at her cousin in sheer amazement. What planet was this girl living on? *'Feel good?'* she repeated, her voice contemptuous. 'Carol, the man is a walking time bomb where women are concerned. You've only to look at him to see that! The only thing that could be added is a big notice on his back with the words ''abandon hope all ye who enter here'' written on it!'

'An unusual suggestion.' His voice was beautifully controlled and as cold as ice. 'But one which I won't be taking up in the immediate future.'

Oh, no. Jessica closed her eyes for a second before nerving herself to turn round. She had seen Carol's eyes widen in the last few seconds as she had spoken but had thought her cousin was shocked at her vehemence. She hadn't known he was right behind her...

'I'm sorry.' There was no way she could brazen it out—she had been as rude as it was possible to be. 'I didn't know you were there,' she added, turning fully to face him.

'I had actually worked that minor detail out for myself.' He was angry—furiously, blazingly angry. But the control still held, she noticed weakly as she took in the expressionless face, his hard eyes resembling two chips of stone-grey granite, and a slash of dull red colour across the high cheekbones giving his gaze a glittering hue. 'But this particular time bomb is not deaf, neither is it stupid. If I were the perfect gentleman, I would now say that I hope you enjoy the rest of your evening and exit on that gracious note—but, unfortunately, I am neither perfect nor, at times, a gentleman. And this is one of those times.'

He'd heard it all, then. Her heart was thudding so hard she wouldn't have been surprised if it had leapt out of her chest.

'You are, without doubt, the most antagonistic, ill-mannered and insulting female I have ever had the misfortune to meet,' he continued with chilling softness. 'But I'm sure I'm not the first male to acquaint you with that fact. Regrettably, you are also one of the loveliest—but not, as I first thought, lovable. Now, having got that off my chest, as it were, I can say in all honesty that I hope you enjoy the rest of your evening.'

She deserved it, that little voice at the back of her mind told her. She thoroughly deserved it. But it still hurt—that 'unlovable' barb hurt more than she could have said. She couldn't speak, couldn't move. She just stared at him with great stricken eyes as he finished his quiet dissection of the fragile façade she had attempted to build in the last few months. And then she turned in one desperate movement and flew across the room, out through the open French doors at the far end and into the dimly lit grounds beyond, not stopping in her head-long dash until she had left all sound and light behind her.

She had heard his muttered 'What the hell…?' in a flash of a moment as she had turned. But even though her head had urged her to stay and see it through, and emerge from the whole miserable encounter with some modicum of self-respect, her heart had been slashed in two at his damning sentence.

She knew she was unlovable; she must be for William to care so little that he'd made her a public spectacle as he'd cast her off and that shattering of her self-esteem and inner core was still an open wound, in spite of her brave protestations to the contrary. She wasn't over William—she'd never be over what he had done to her—and Jo… Oh, Jo, how could you have done this to me? she cried silently. How could you have planned it, anticipated it?

She flung herself down onto the bowling-green smooth grass a good way from the house in a small natural arbour of trees and sweet-smelling flowering bushes, quite unable to control the sobs that were racking her body in an agony of grief. She didn't want to cry; she had wasted enough energy on that very thing—more than enough. And she didn't want to feel like this; it was so *unfair*. She hadn't done anything—she was the one who was innocent. So why was all the pain and agony on her shoulders, William and Jo having got off scot-free? They were enjoying life—together—and she'd been left a physical and mental wreck. Oh, it just wasn't *fair*…

When the hand first touched her shoulder she thought it was Carol—gentle, faithful Carol, coming to find her. But she was quite unable to respond to the tender touch. Half of her was angry, furiously, wildly angry with her-self for not coping better, and the other—the other just wanted to howl and kick and scream against all the broken dreams, the pain, the betrayal that were still a physical ache, day and night.

'Come on, come on.' She didn't recognise the soft masculine voice, but when she was lifted from the ground and cradled in a pair of hard-muscled arms her senses identified the smell and feel of him. *Colt Irons.* Oh, no, not Colt Irons. Carol wouldn't have let him see her like this, not Colt Irons.

'I'm sorry, Jessica; I didn't know about your fiancé,' he said now, still in the same quiet, soft voice.

Carol had told him? It was like a bucket of cold water and brought the storm of weeping to hiccuping sobs almost in the same breath as the awful realisation hit her. Carol had told Colt Irons she'd been jilted at the altar? She wouldn't—she couldn't have.

Jessica kept her head buried against the hard wall of his chest for one more moment, seeking courage to lift her wet face and meet his gaze, and then she looked up slowly, her face washed with tears and her hair tangled silver about her neck. 'What...what do you mean?' she murmured weakly, her pulse quickening in spite of herself at the sight of him.

'Carol explained your wedding was called off at the last moment, a few months ago, that your fiancé had met someone else.'

Well, that was one way of putting it, she thought bleakly as she tried to gather what was left of her shredded dignity about her. 'I see.' Her voice was quiet and flat and very small.

'I wouldn't have been so...abrasive if I'd known,' he added gently.

It was the gentleness that did it, indicating as it did that he was feeling sorry for her. She knew, she just knew, that he was the type of man who would rarely, if ever, apologise, and for him to do so now meant he was pitying her. Oh, she couldn't bear it. She'd had enough of people doing that to last her a lifetime. They didn't need to feel sorry for her—*he* didn't need to feel sorry for her; she wasn't some little scrap of flotsam and jet-sam that the tide had washed in. She would survive this and prove everyone wrong. *She would.*

'Are you saying that your words were uncalled for?' she challenged now, stepping back a pace as she attempted to undo what was left of the knot on the top of her head and comb out the pale silk of her hair with her fingers. She didn't know her chin had gone up a notch, wasn't aware of the way her eyes had suddenly sparked with a mixture of mortification and embarrassment, but the man standing in front of her read the signals accurately.

Well, she had guts, he had to give her that, even if she was a little fireball on legs. 'No.' He stared at her, his eyes narrowing on the sensual fullness of her mouth. 'I'm not saying that. You *are* antagonistic and insulting and ill-mannered. I'm merely saying that I can see you might have some justification for it, that's all.'

'I thought you said you didn't go in for graciousness?' she said sarcastically, pure adrenalin sweeping the weakness from her limbs and clearing her head, as well as cauterising the desire to cry.

'I said I wasn't perfect,' he corrected her softly, 'or a gentleman. Even a low-life like me can be gracious on occasion.'

The mockery was provoking, but it wasn't that which was causing her blood to tinge her face with pink. It was him, the sheer overwhelming animal magnetism of him. She'd felt it that afternoon amongst the coconut shies and gaily dressed crowds. But here in the dark of the night, with the moonlight shadowing his face into harsh planes and valleys, he seemed dangerous. Frighteningly dangerous. Thrillingly dangerous. And all male. Definitely all male.

'I don't need your graciousness,' she said proudly, lifting her head still higher in an unconscious repudiation of the intimidation that powerful, broad-shouldered body was sending to hers. 'I was wrong and I admit I shouldn't have said those things in front of you.'

'Ah, but you didn't know I was in earshot, did you?' he countered softly. 'So that makes it all right?' It was a question, not a statement, and she stared at him for a moment, her mind racing. 'You think the content, at least, was justified?'

'Are you saying I was wrong? That you don't have lots of women?' she asked carefully, to break the silence that was charged with something which positively crackled.

'I wasn't aware I had to explain my love life to a total stranger one way or the other.' His voice was silky, the sort of raw silkiness that disguised cold steel. 'I don't know what you've heard, or from whom, and frankly I don't care. It's absolutely none of your business.'

He didn't mince his words. She continued to run her fingers through her hair, the indigo sky overhead, in which the full moon sat with queenly radiance, giving her ash-blonde tresses a halo of white gold. 'Then I was right,' she said flatly.

He swore, a particularly explicit profanity that caused her to wince. So it was all the more surprising when he spoke next and his voice was soft and thick. 'Do you still love him?'

'What?' She was stung into shocked outrage.

'This fool who let you go, do you still love him?' he persisted quietly.

She couldn't believe he had just asked her that and she said so, her voice shaking. 'How dare you ask me that? You've no right.'

'If I'd waited until I was given my rights most of the opportunities that have proved rewarding in my life would have passed me by.' He moved closer now, and tension snaked down her spine as he lifted a hand to her cheek, brushing a strand of hair from her stricken face. 'I don't know many women who can howl like you've just done and still look good,' he said conversationally, his voice unforgivably detached. 'Is he worth it? Have you asked yourself if he's worth all this anguish?'

'Now look—'

'Or are you so caught up in the web of self-pity that logic doesn't apply?' His eyes had fastened on her mouth again and she actually shivered at their brooding power. 'Grieving has its place…' She thought for a moment that a shadow passed over the hard, cruel face but then as the trees moved in the whispering breeze she decided it had been a trick of the moonlight. 'But, like everything beneficial, too much can be bad for you. It's time you moved into the real world again.'

'Is it indeed?' She glared at him, furious that he thought he could analyse her after two meetings and even more furious that he was right. 'It's as easy as that, is it?'

'I didn't say it was easy but it sure beats locking yourself away in an ivory tower.' The ruthless, cynical face had an expression she couldn't quite define but, with him so close, coherent thought was beginning to be less and less an option.

'I haven't locked myself away. I'm here tonight, aren't I?' She said it with a flourish, like a magician producing a rabbit out of a hat, and for a moment the austere lines of his features relaxed as his mouth twitched.

'Crying buckets in the garden?' He shook his head. 'Sorry, that doesn't count.'

'What does count, then?'

'This.' His mouth was knowing as it took hers, and this time his hands brushed over her in a seductively light caress that made her breath catch in her throat in a tiny gasp.

'Don't.' As his mouth moved to her eyes and ears, in tiny feather-light kisses that caused an immediate response deep in her lower stomach, she formed the word on a whispered plea. But he merely settled her closer into his muscled hardness, the alien lines of his body powerful and strong.

Like before she sensed the skill in his mastery over her senses and she wanted to fight it; she really did. But the strangest sensation of hot, overwhelmingly delicious desire was coursing through her veins like wildfire. She had never felt this way before, not with William, not with anyone. It was intoxicating…

When his lips moved to hers again, parting them as he penetrated her mouth with an ease that she kicked herself for afterwards, she felt as though she was melting into him, losing herself, becoming absorbed in the whole of him.

She couldn't allow this to continue. The thought was there, but somewhere far away, blanketed by what was happening to her body. She didn't know him, for goodness' sake. By his own admission he was a virtual stranger. She couldn't let him…subject her like this. But the mantle of darkness was heavy and warm, the scents of summer sweet on the night air, and she sighed softly against his breath, her hands clinging onto the broad, hard shoulders as the kiss became even more intimate. Reason was an enemy who had no place in the enchantment she was experiencing.

'He must have been crazy. You're so sweet, so desirable…' The kiss became urgent, fierce now, and as he moulded her against him she could feel the arousal he was making no effort to hide. He wanted her, this powerful, wealthy man who had only to click his fingers and see a hundred beautiful women jump. He wanted *her*. But in the same instant she realised she had been drugged by the sensual chemistry that had her in its grip—this terrifying mastery over her emotions and her body that he seemed to induce so effortlessly. She couldn't do this, mustn't…

'No!' As she wrenched herself away he made no movement to stop her, and, perversely, she felt quite bereft at his acceptance of her refusal to go any further.

What was happening to her? she asked herself helplessly, aware she was panting wildly, her eyes fixed on
his as she fought for control. How could she feel such
excitement, such desire, for a man she didn't know and
didn't like? Was this the traditional rebound scenario?
The falling out of one man's bed into another? But she
hadn't been in William's bed, had she? She hadn't been
in any man's bed if it came to that, although she must
have given Colt Irons quite a different impression.

One black eyebrow lifted upwards in cool derision at
her panic. 'Let go of him, Jessica,' he said calmly, as
though they were continuing a conversation that had
been interrupted by nothing more eventful than a sneeze.
'Start to live again.'

'Look, you know nothing about it so please cut the
psychoanalysis.'' His face hardened and she added
quickly, 'I'd better get back now. Carol will be worried.'

'Damn Carol.' He moved a couple of paces to a cop-
per beech tree, crossing his arms in brooding contem-
plation as he leant lazily against its trunk. 'Right, I know
nothing about it, so tell me.'

'I don't want to,' she said a little desperately.

'Why? Because you'd rather bury yourself out here in
the middle of nowhere for the rest of your life?' he asked
caustically.

'I don't live here.' She saw the eyebrows lift further
and kicked herself for the slip. She didn't want him to
know anything about her, anything at all, and already
she'd admitted that the little Kent village wasn't her
home.

'No?' His tone invited further confidence, but she totally ignored it.

'No.' She knew she was glaring at him but she
couldn't control the antagonism of which he'd accused
her earlier. He was so assertive and dominant—as well
as insultingly impertinent—and his authority and coolness grated on her more than she would ever have
thought possible.

How on earth had she got herself into this ridiculous position? she thought angrily as she stared at him through the shadowed night. There he was, the very picture of a man contentedly at peace with himself and master of his surroundings and those he came into contact with. He exuded self-satisfaction and just at the moment it caught her on the raw.

'You aren't making this easy.' He raked back his hair with a gesture that spoke of sudden impatience and the movement brought a whiff of expensive and sensual aftershave to the air, at the same time emphasising powerful chest muscles under the snowy white dinner shirt he was wearing.

'I didn't know I had to.' She tried for a lift of the eyebrows herself in an expression she hoped came across as cool and mocking but which, she suspected from the look on his face, was merely fatuous.

'Have it your own way,' he said grimly, straightening from his lounging position in a manner that indicated enough was enough. 'But just remember you aren't the first woman to be let down by a smooth-talking rat who promised the moon and couldn't come up with the goods. How old are you? Nineteen, twenty?'

'I'm twenty-four,' she said tightly. 'Not that it's any of your business.' She resented the implication that she was wallowing in self-pity almost as much as she resented the man himself.

'Then you've the whole of your life in front of you, for crying out loud,' he said crisply. 'And I'd say you've spent enough time crying over spilt milk.'

'Oh, would you indeed?' The cheek, the *incredible* cheek of him! 'Well, perhaps some of us can't turn our emotions on and off like a tap—have you considered that point in all these clichés you seem to love so much? I thought I was going to spend the rest of my life with William, I was committed to him and our future and then it all ended in a moment. Now you might be able to bounce right back after something like that but I can't.'

'And you've made up your mind about that, haven't you?' the hateful voice continued. 'Poor little Jessica Taylor, crossed in love—'

'I'm not listening to any more of this,' she said furiously, her voice simmering with anger. 'I'm going back to the house.'

'Because you know I'm right.'

And as she swung to face him again the mocking note in the dark, dry voice pushed her over the edge. All the rage and fury she had been banking down for months exploded in a white-hot torrent she couldn't have prevented if she'd wanted to. 'No, you aren't right,' she spat loudly, her voice shaking with outrage. 'You aren't right at all. You think I merely lost William and I ought to be over it by now—but it was more, much more than that. He didn't just finish our engagement, nothing as kind as that! He actually let me turn up at the church on my wedding day to find he had run off with someone else that very morning.'

'Jessica—'

'No, you wanted to hear it, so damn well listen!' She was past anything now but the anger that was consuming her, and although he had moved just in front of her he made no attempt to touch her, realising some sort of emotional dam had broken. 'And do you want to know who that someone was? Do you? Of course you do. They all did; it was the talk of the town for weeks. It was my chief bridesmaid, as it happens. Isn't that funny? Don't you think it's funny, Mr Know-It-All Colt Irons? And she was chief bridesmaid because she is my sister. That added a nice touch to the scandal, along with the fact that she was three months pregnant at the time. All in all it was quite a day to remember, my wedding that never was.'

He said nothing but she had the dubious satisfaction of seeing his eyes widen with shock before he narrowed them to stare penetratingly into her flushed face.

'So when you talk about being crossed in love you're

right—dead right. Only it wasn't just William who crossed me. It was my sister too, aided and abetted by my mother, who couldn't bear the fact I had chosen to live with my father and not her when they split up ten years ago.'

There was silence for a long, taut moment and then he spoke slowly, his body perfectly still as he said, 'Do you know that for certain? About your mother, I mean?'

'Yes.' The word was a snap into the space between them.

'I see.' And now the quietness stretched and tightened and she knew she had to break it before he spoke again. There had been too many words over the last five months as it was, from her father—whose grief and pain had almost matched her own—from her mother, well-meaning friends and relatives, workmates... Words, words, words, until she could have screamed and beaten her fists against their uselessness. And from the two people at the heart of her misery? Silence. Cruel, uncaring silence—but then what could they say after all?

'I'm going back to the house now and I would prefer to go alone.' Her voice was cold and clipped. It was the only way she could survive the humiliation of what she had revealed to him.

He didn't speak or try to stop her, for which she was eternally grateful. He merely nodded abruptly as she turned to leave, her head high and her back straight.

She pleaded a headache and left the party almost immediately, adding her support to Harry's insistence that Carol stay for a while. She wanted to be alone; more than anything she wanted to be alone. Which was crazy, really, when loneliness was a dark, chilling spectre at her shoulder day and night.

But she had to be able to be quiet and think, play the last hour over and over in her mind as she sorted out her whirling thoughts, not the least of which was how on earth could she be physically attracted to someone she barely knew and didn't like?

She took in an urgent breath of air in the dark interior of the taxi as it sped through the night. Colt Irons had been playing with her that afternoon, amusing himself like the lord of the manor with a peasant girl, and tonight he had thought he could do the same—but he'd got more than he'd bargained for, she thought grimly.

He was wealthy beyond the normal man's wildest dreams. Powerful, handsome in a cruel, aggressive sort of way, and although she hated to admit it there was something else—a double—no, *triple* dose of everything that made a man a man in every line of that muscled body and ruthless face. So why, when he could have any woman he wanted with one crook of his little finger, had he bothered with her in the first place tonight? As if she didn't know...

Her face turned scarlet as she recalled their conversation that afternoon and his lovemaking that night. He had thought she was easy; that much was obvious. She ground her teeth in impotent fury, her eyes narrowing at the dark world outside.

'Satisfaction Guaranteed'. He'd seen that silly poster that Carol had put up for a bit of fun and thought it was an invitation. But she couldn't blame her cousin, not really. The afternoon was one thing, but the way she had responded to him that night... It was only the taxi driver's eyes in the mirror that kept her from groaning out loud. And then to go and tell him the whole sordid catalogue of events—she must have been mad—stark, staring mad! Thank goodness she would never have to see him again. She sank back in the seat as she raised two hands to her burning cheeks. He must think she was a cross between a raging nymphomaniac and a candidate for the nut house, and just at the moment she couldn't have put up a plausible argument to the contrary.

She repeated the excuse of a sudden headache to her aunt and uncle, who were watching television in their pretty cottage-style lounge and who stared at her, amazed, as she returned barely an hour or so after leaving. She then went straight up to the small spare room she was occupying, claiming she needed an early night.

What a disaster of a weekend! After a quick shower she sat cross-legged on the bed, combing through her damp hair as she let her thoughts have free rein. And she still had all day tomorrow to get through until she could leave to catch her train at five o'clock. He wouldn't try to see her, would he? The possibility brought her bolt upright for a moment before she relaxed again.

Of course he won't—don't be so daft, Jess, she told herself irritably. Even his ego, jumbo-sized though it was, would accept defeat after what she'd told him tonight.

She lay back against the pillows, spreading her hair fan-wise in a pale arc behind her, unable to stop her mind dissecting every word they had spoken, every caress and embrace they'd shared.

She was still wide awake, lying in the darkness with her window open to the cool night air, when Carol arrived home at just after midnight. She suspected Harry had driven her—the car stayed outside too long for a taxi—and, after it had roared off into the night and Carol had quietly let herself into the house, she heard her cousin pause for some seconds outside her door and then continue along the landing to her own room.

Oh, this was ridiculous! She plumped her pillows fiercely before concentrating her mind on sleep. She wasn't going to think about Colt Irons any more. He was now in the past along with the humiliation of the evening, and that was that!

And it wasn't until some time later—days, in fact—that she realized that that night was the first one since the ill-fated day in January, when her world and her heart had been ripped apart, that she had gone to sleep without being tormented by a thousand burning images of Jo locked in William's arms—of them walking, talking together as they shared what should have been hers.

CHAPTER THREE

'JESSICA?' The deep, husky voice was unmistakable and she gripped the phone tightly, her eyes widening with shock. 'I'm in your neck of the woods for a day or two and I wondered if you're free for dinner tonight?'

'I...' She tried to speak, tried to formulate the refusal in her head into recognisable words, but her brain seemed to have frozen.

'It's Colt Irons,' he continued smoothly, after waiting a moment.

She knew who it was! She bit her lip hard, willing the pain to cut through her stunned surprise and provide the necessary adrenalin. It worked.

'Colt Irons?' She allowed her voice to register the faintest perplexity and then said, 'Oh, yes, of course, I remember. I met you at a party some weeks ago?'

'That's right.' The dark voice was mockingly silky, his tone telling her quite clearly that she hadn't fooled him for a minute. 'I was staying with the Brindales for the weekend,' he supplied helpfully, the mockery even more pronounced as he emphasised the name, 'but we met at a fête in the afternoon first. You were...obliging at a stall?'

'Yes.' The word was a quick snap and she could have kicked herself in the next moment for rising to the none too subtle bait. 'Yes, of course,' she said more slowly, 'but there were so many people there...'

'Weren't there.' His voice was an amused drawl. 'I hope you don't mind me ringing like this, Jessica?'

Mind? Of course she minded. 'Not at all.' She forced her voice into a bland, social coolness that was polite, no more. 'How did you get my number? From Carol?'

'No…' There was a pregnant pause. 'Strangely, your cousin seems to have some sort of amnesia when it comes to telephone numbers.'

Good old Carol! Jessica felt a lightning stab of guilt for having doubted her.

'But a little detective work and here we are,' he continued smoothly. 'I'm not easily daunted, although your home number seemed to be untraceable. However, Carol had mentioned to Harry who you worked for in London and as luck would have it I'm looking for someone reliable to market a little project of mine. I take it your boss *is* reliable?' he asked blandly.

'What? Oh, yes—yes, of course.' She could hardly believe her ears.

'And while we were talking business I remembered to ask for your home number—' his voice was heavy with treacly innocence '—which Russell was only too pleased to supply. He seemed…surprised that we were acquainted.'

Jessica moved the phone away from her ear and stared, frowning at the receiver. Now what was all that supposed to imply? Was he telling the truth when he said he had some business to put Russell's way? It seemed the height of vanity to think it was all a ploy to meet her again—she frowned at the phone—yes, it was; of course it was. Colt Irons didn't have to chase after a woman—any woman. From what she had read and heard it was very much the other way round. She really had to pull herself together.

'So, are you free tonight?' he continued after another small pause.

'I…I'm sorry—'

'Because it would be a good opportunity to put you in the picture about the project,' he added silkily. 'I understand you work very closely with Russell on most things?'

'Yes, I do, but—'

'And there is nothing like a face-to-face meeting to

emphasise exactly what's required. Unfortunately I shall be tied up for the rest of my time in London and I fly out to France Thursday morning.'

'Oh.' She glanced round the somewhat dingy hall helplessly. When another of the residents of the house had knocked a few minutes earlier to tell her she was wanted on the phone, moments after she had shut her front door after getting home from work, the very last thing she had expected was an invitation to dinner from Colt Irons. 'Well, I suppose if it's business...'

She realised the moment after the words had left her lips that they sounded grudging, and his voice reflected his appreciation of the fact as he said, 'Thank you, that's most magnanimous of you, Jessica. Shall we say eight o'clock, then? Russell gave me your address.'

Here? He wanted to come and pick her up here? She looked at the peeling wallpaper and said hastily, 'I can meet you; there's no need to put yourself out—'

'Eight o'clock, Jessica.' And the line went dead.

'Oh, hell.' She glared at the inoffensive receiver before replacing it none too gently on the wall. 'I don't believe this.'

She continued to talk to herself in fits and starts all the time she got ready, drinking several cups of strong black coffee in an effort to calm her nerves. She phoned Russell at home, who confirmed everything that Colt had told her, and seemed inordinately pleased that his personal assistant knew such an influential name in the city.

'Why didn't you tell me, Jess?' he asked reproachfully, his tone indicating she had let him down badly by the omission.

'I...I forgot.' It was weak but all she could manage.

'You forgot? Jess, you forget to pick up the laundry, or put the cat out, or a hundred and one other things that make up normal life, but you don't forget meeting Colt Irons.'

You can say that again, she thought balefully, gritting

her teeth before saying, 'Well I did. I'm sorry, but I just forgot.'

She heard Monica, Russell's young and very pregnant wife, say something in the background and his voice was apologetic when he next spoke. 'Well, you've had a lot on your plate recently. At least you put in a plug for the firm, anyway, which is the main thing.'

'Did Colt say that?' she asked carefully.

'I think so.' His voice was slightly puzzled. 'Why?'

'No reason. I'll see you tomorrow, anyway, Russell, and we'll go over everything.'

'Fine. Take care.'

Take care? Oh, she'd take care all right, she thought testily as she pulled every last strand of hair into a tight knot at the back of her head. The long-sleeved, high-cut black cocktail dress she was wearing added to the efficient, businesslike image that stared back at her from the full-length mirror on the wall.

She couldn't blame Russell's note of disbelief when he had questioned her overlooking Colt Irons. It was true—you didn't forget a meeting with him in a hurry. In fact she had thought of little else for the last few weeks. She had been in a fever of fearful anticipation that Sunday morning at Carol's house, jumping every time the phone had rung and diving up to her room on the two occasions someone had knocked on the door.

But he hadn't called or phoned, and by the time she had caught the train that evening she'd been berating herself for thinking he would bother with a little nobody like her. And she didn't want him to, she *didn't*, she told herself now for the hundredth time since that weekend in Brindale. It was the last thing she wanted.

She didn't like hard, aggressive men—she never had, preferring males who met her as an equal, saw her as a *person* first and foremost, the romantic side being a very definite second to friendship and companionship. William had been like that. She stopped fiddling with her hair as she contemplated her ex-fiancé. He had been gentle and kind and...weak? The thought came from no-where and hit her straight between the eyes. Weak? William wasn't weak, he was... Well, he was...

She stared at her reflection, her mind racing, but then the ringing of the doorbell downstairs brought her springing into action as she grabbed her bag and made for the stairs before someone else answered the door. Colt Irons in her little bedsit? Never.

'Jessica...' As she opened the front door she blessed the little dart of intuition that had warned her moments before to keep her expression under strict control. He looked devastating. His dinner suit was plain but exqui-sitely cut over the broad, wide shoulders and big chest, the cream shirt and bow-tie accentuating his dark mas-culinity in a way that made her palms damp and her mouth dry. The black hair did the same, slicked back ruthlessly from his brow, from under which hard grey eyes surveyed her with an intentness that made her wish she hadn't dressed so severely, had allowed herself a softer hairstyle, more make-up. But she didn't want to give him the wrong impression, she told herself fiercely, not after Brindale. 'You look enchanting, and very ef-ficient.'

He'd guessed, then? Sensed what she was trying to state? She kept her face blank by sheer will-power, tak-ing a long, calming breath of air and smiling politely. 'Good evening, Mr Irons.'

'Colt, please,' he interjected smoothly.

'Oh, but if I'm going to work for you...'

'Colt.' He smiled, but she knew he had acknowledged her reminder of their boss-employee relationship by the thinning of the cruel mouth and momentary narrowing of the lethal eyes.

She wasn't an easy lay, whatever impression she might have given to the contrary that day and evening—*oh, the evening*—in June. And if he thought she was ready and available he had another think coming.

'Colt.' She smiled warily, satisfied her point had been

made, and then her eyes opened wide with surprise as he brought a small box from behind his back. 'Oh, it's beautiful.' The corsage was a mixture of tiny white orchids and rosebuds, the velvet petals just touched with the faintest shade of pink, and the harsh mouth softened at her obvious delight in the flowers.

'Allow me.' He was quite proper when he fixed the tiny bouquet just above her left breast but it took every ounce of will-power she possessed to stand still as his firm fingers deftly pinned the flowers in place, and her cheeks were burning by the time he had finished. 'Shall we?' He took her arm as they walked down the three or four steps from the front door, indicating a long, low, sleek monster of a car over on the other side of the road with a casual flick of his head.

She hardly knew how to walk as they crossed the quiet street, but hiding her gaucherie, she put steel in her backbone as she slipped into the luxurious interior of the Ferrari, Colt joining her in the beautiful car after shutting her door. He was the only man she had ever met who could make her knees go weak just with the sheer sensual smell of him, she thought helplessly as the big body slid into the leather seat beside hers. Did he know? Was he aware of the devastating effect he had on women?

Oh, for goodness' sake, Jessica, why ask the road you know? She glared angrily out of the low windscreen as the ignition flared into life, only to turn to him in surprise when the powerful engine died again. 'What's the matter?'

'You're the matter.' It was said lazily but with an undeniable thread of steel running through the attractive voice.

'Me?' She stared at him indignantly, her velvet brown eyes wide. 'What have I done?'

'Do you mean besides coming to the door with every possible inch of skin hidden from view, and your hair screwed back so tightly you're going to have a blinding headache by the end of the evening?' he asked conversationally. 'Jumping like a cat on a hot tin roof every time I so much as touch you, staring at me out of great reproachful brown eyes that accuse me of crimes so varied I would have to have been on this earth at least half a dozen lifetimes to manage to commit them all?'

'You're being ridiculous—'

'And then scowling ahead, your body as stiff as a board, with your face matching any gargoyles I've ever seen for sheer fierceness?' He paused, the thick, curling black eyelashes she remembered so well flicking down over the laser-sharpness of his eyes for one moment before lifting as he surveyed her again, a slight twist of a smile at his mouth now. 'You mean besides those trifles?'

'I...I didn't—'

'I'm not going to hurt you, Jessica.' He leant towards her and it would have taken more control than she possessed not to jerk slightly as his hands took hers, her reaction registering in the hard line of his mouth. 'You see?' he added slowly. 'What the hell have you heard about me anyway? I doubt if the Marquis de Sade himself got such a response from his women.'

His women? And she didn't doubt it was women, plural—*definitely* plural—with Colt Irons. The thought shouldn't have rankled the way it did.

'We are going to have dinner, discuss some work, and then I'm going to deliver you home, safe and sound, with your honour intact,' he said lazily. 'If I wanted to take a woman into my bed tonight there are any number of females I could call who would be only too happy to oblige.' Her head shot up to meet his eyes and he smiled sardonically at her outraged expression. 'So why don't you try to relax and enjoy yourself?' he continued smoothly. 'It's going to kill my reputation as the big bad wolf and despoiler of virgins if you persist in wearing that expression of furious dignity all evening.'

She didn't like the dry, mocking tone of that husky

voice and sure enough, as she glanced at his mouth, she saw it was twitching with barely concealed amusement. He found her funny!

Colt turned and started the engine and when she found she was glaring at the hard profile again she quickly schooled her features into a more acceptable mask. She was blowed if she was going to give him room for any more of those dry, cynical comments he did so well. From now on she would be polite, coolly charming and very businesslike, as befitted Russell's advocate. But it wouldn't be easy.

As it happened she was perfectly right. The small, select restaurant was the sort of exclusive place where only the most influential names ate, and consequently both the food and the service were first-class. It was indicative of the clientele that no prices were printed on the elaborate menus, which were exquisite works of art in themselves. And it was even more indicative of Colt Irons' standing in the order of things that the head waiter nearly fell over himself in ingratiating homage as he showed them to a secluded table for two, situated in a gracious alcove where they could see but not be seen.

'Champagne cocktail?' She nodded smilingly and Colt turned to the little man hovering at his shoulder. 'One of your special cocktails for Miss Taylor, Claude, and a mineral water for me, I'm afraid. I'm driving.'

'Certainly, certainly.' The said Claude bowed himself away smilingly after personally placing the menus in their hands.

'Would you like to wait a while before we order?' Colt asked courteously. 'And enjoy a couple of drinks first?'

'Not really.' The food looked wonderful, from what she had seen of it as Claude had shown them to their table, and it had made her realise just how hungry she was. 'I'm absolutely starving, to be honest.'

'Are you?' He looked pleased if surprised. 'I was

afraid, with the sort of figure you've got, you were one of those women who nibble at lettuce leaves all day.'

'Not me,' she said definitely. 'I eat like a horse, I'm afraid, but I seem to have the sort of metabolism that burns it all off just as quickly. The job helps; we run about like chickens with our heads cut off most days.'

'Ah, yes, the job.' He indicated the menu in her hand. 'Decide what you'd like and then we'll have that chat about this new venture of mine, okay?' His smile was warm and she felt the impact of it right down to her toes.

'Fine.' She managed a smile in return and then buried her face in the menu until the burning colour in her cheeks had subsided. She had to stop this; it was ridiculous! She had to be able to speak to him without turning the colour of a boiled lobster. It was embarrassingly schoolgirlish and not at all the impression she was trying to put over to an astute man of the world like him.

But he was just so overwhelming. It wasn't so bad when he was being cold and mocking and she could work up some rage and indignation as protection against that powerful magnetism he exuded so naturally, but that smile had been a whole different ball game. Nevertheless, she had to be in control, *would* be in control. He was just a man like any other...

When Claude returned with the drinks she was sufficiently composed to give her choice of dishes with a cool equanimity and poise that suggested she ate in places like this, with handsome millionaire escorts, every night of the week. And that was how she had to be, she told herself firmly, taking a long sip of the delicious pink cocktail before steeling herself to look directly into his face. Fate had decreed that for the next few years she was going to concentrate on her career and nothing else as she pulled together her shattered self-esteem and rebuilt her life.

A business contact like Colt Irons could do Russell's little company nothing but good—and if he prospered she prospered; it was as simple as that. As Russell's personal assistant she had to make sure she was one hundred per cent competent and adaptable and she would do it right now if it killed her.

On meeting the slate-grey eyes she saw the gleam of amusement was back. 'Okay, let's have it. What are you thinking now to put that fierceness in your face?' he asked lazily.

'What? Oh, nothing.' She straightened her face but it was too late. 'I...I was just thinking that we'll do our very best on this project of yours,' she said quietly, deciding that in this instance honesty was the best policy. She didn't want him thinking she was scowling at him again. 'I didn't know I was looking fierce,' she added weakly.

His eyes narrowed slightly, his expression very intent as he considered her words, and then he leant towards her as the devastating smile came into play again. 'I'm sure you'll do your best, Jessica,' he said softly, 'but perhaps you'd better hear it first and we'll go from there?'

She took another sip of the cocktail and nodded with serious concentration. 'Right.'

'As you might or might not know I have fingers in several different pies.' She nodded again, her brain registering that she was seeing a new side to him as he went into work mode, his mind totally absorbed in what he was saying, the grey eyes razor-sharp with an intelligence that was intimidating.

'A business associate in Scotland, who is also a friend, has approached me with a partnership deal on a new venture which I consider most interesting. What do you know about aggregate?' he asked suddenly.

'Not much,' she admitted frankly, 'although Russell said—' She stopped abruptly as the keen eyes homed in.

'You've spoken to Russell about this?' His voice was quite expressionless.

'Yes.' She stared at him defiantly. There was no reason why she shouldn't, was there? 'I rang him tonight.'

'Checking up on me?' he asked silkily. 'Well, that's good—thorough. I like that.' She felt somehow it wasn't the total truth. 'And what did Russell say exactly?'

'Very little. Just that this was a new project for you which involved moving millions of tons of stone. He said…he said you'd explain tonight.'

He inclined his head as he said, 'Just so. Basically, the world needs aggregate. Hard stone like gravel and granite can be crushed into anything from powder dust to pebbles and used in the construction of buildings, roads. You get my drift?' She nodded carefully, determining to let him do all the talking.

'The proposal is that we basically remove a mountain, the area of which is accessible only by helicopter or sea—there are no roads—and transport the stone to a deep-water quay where a specially developed ship will be waiting. The ship is quite revolutionary in design, developed and equipped specially for this project, with hoppers that are shaped like a funnel at the bottom. Underneath each funnel outlet is a huge conveyor belt which carries the stone out and up to be dumped on the quayside when it reaches its destination. Simple, eh?' His voice was mocking and she guessed the concept was mind-blowing to brains with technical knowledge.

'The area we're considering in Scotland is one where nothing grows or grazes,' he continued quietly. 'Very remote and barren, so there is no question of destroying the environment. The conveyors will be enclosed, limiting dust fallout in the area, which is completely unpopulated.'

'I see.' She stared back into the dark face opposite her, her mind absorbing the content of his words. 'It seems a very good idea.'

'It is.' He smiled lazily and leant back in his chair, running a hand through his hair as he took a sip of his drink. 'And hopefully a very lucrative one, which is where you and Russell come in. I'd like you to establish the market for potential buyers both in England and Europe, but especially abroad. Russell tells me you are fluent in French and German with a knowledge of Italian and Spanish? That's quite an arsenal; how did that come about?'

'What?' The sudden switch onto a more personal level momentarily threw her. 'Oh, my father was a marine biologist,' she said hastily. 'Well, he still is; he's working on something in the Caribbean at the moment. His work meant we moved all round the world when I was growing up so I went to school in umpteen different countries.'

'That must have been very difficult for you,' he said quietly, watching her face with piercing eyes.

'Not really.' She shrugged gracefully. 'I never found languages a problem; I seem to be able to pick them up almost immediately somehow. But it was worse for my sister and mother. They didn't enjoy the moving about.'

'And you did?' He had leant forward again, his gaze very intent as he registered every tiny change in her face.

'Yes, I think so—it never bothered me anyway. I'm very fond of my father—' She stopped abruptly, realising she was saying too much. She didn't want a personal relationship with this man, not even in the remotest way, and the less he knew about her the better.

'Go on.' His voice was very soft and very deep.

'There's nothing more to say,' she said brightly. 'That's how I came to speak my languages, that's all.'

'And your parents split up when you were fourteen?' he persisted gently.

'Yes.' She looked down at the blindingly white linen tablecloth, hoping he would take the hint and return to the proposed project. He didn't.

'Why?' The dark voice held a deadly tenacity.

'Why? My mother found someone else—the usual thing,' she said, with a brittle nonchalance that didn't fool the keen grey eyes for a moment. 'She returned home to England with her new love and…and my sister. I stayed in the States with my father. They… It was a very bitter divorce and I'd rather not discuss it any more,' she added in a little rush.

He chose to completely ignore her last words as he said, 'And you think your mother resents the fact you chose to live with your father?'

'No, I don't think it, I know it,' she said in a little flat voice that made his mouth tighten. 'She wanted to take everything from him, strip him of all the things he held dear, and she didn't like it when I wouldn't play ball.'

'And does your father think your mother encouraged this…alliance between your fiancé and sister?' he asked very quietly.

'He…' She paused and shook her head before saying, 'My father always thinks the best of everyone; he doesn't know my mother like I do.'

'After being married to her for at least fourteen years?' he queried with a cynicism that grated on her stretched nerves like barbed wire.

'They were married for sixteen years and, yes, in spite of that,' she said stiffly, her eyes cold and angry now at what she saw as his defence of her mother. This was nothing to do with him; how dared he make a judgement? she asked herself hotly. Prospective juicy job or not, she wasn't standing any more of this. 'And I don't like your tone, Mr Irons,' she added bravely, her eyes holding his as her stomach turned over at her own audacity.

She expected some sort of cutting retort, one of the lacerating observations that he did so well and with such piercing effect. So she was left open-mouthed when he continued staring at her for a full thirty seconds before stretching slightly as he leant back in his chair and said, with a total lack of expression, 'Others have said the same.'

She was saved from sitting there with her mouth open, searching desperately for something to say, by the waiter arriving with the first course, and she had never been so glad to see anyone in her life. The waiter busied himself serving the carrot, watercress and orange salad she had ordered, Colt having chosen a mushroom and baked ham soufflé. The awkwardness of the moment passed and for a few minutes they both concentrated on the excellent food.

By the time the second course of sole with fennel and soured cream sauce was in front of them Colt had metamorphosed into the perfect dinner companion, his conversation light and witty and his manner pleasant. Although Jessica wasn't fooled by the apparent transformation of the ruthless, hard individual she had come to know, it made a pleasant change, and one she could go along with until the meal was finished.

If only he wasn't so attractive, she thought musingly, applying herself with some relish to a forkful of lemonglazed carrots that tasted heavenly. But 'attractive' was too weak a word to apply to Colt Irons. She glanced at him from under her eyelashes. His face was too dark and compelling, his big body too powerful, with its tightly packed muscles and massive bone structure, to call attractive. Hypnotic, ruthless, devastating, frightening... Yes, definitely frightening, she decided silently. That was an adjective she could acquiesce to. He wasn't a comfortable man to be with...

But then she'd had comfort. William had been comfortable and look where that had got her. The thought brought her eyes wide open and she purposely blanked her mind from further reflections, spearing a succulent morsel of sole with unnecessary force.

Later, when the chocolate terrine ribboned in caramel approached their table, Jessica was full, but the sight of the mouth-watering dessert was too tempting to refuse. 'That was really gorgeous; thank you, Colt,' she sighed appreciatively as she finished the last delicious spoonful a few minutes later.

'My pleasure,' he said with lazy amusement. 'It makes

a refreshing change to see a woman enjoy her food like you do.'

Refreshing change? she thought immediately. From what? Or from whom, more to the point! Still, it's none of your business, Jess. The silent admonition was charged with warning. The last thing she needed right now was the light flirtation Carol had suggested that June day some weeks ago, even if Colt was inclined to dally with her for a while, which she doubted. He had contacted her again because of the Scotland project, that was all, and anything else was strictly in her imagination. She could conceive that he liked his women in the same mould as his car—fast, spectacular and problem-free—and she didn't qualify on any count.

'So, what do you think?' For an awful moment she thought he had read her mind and then, with a sagging of her body she couldn't hide, she realised he was talking about the proposed venture.

'It seems a wonderful opportunity and I'm sure we can do a good job for you,' she said quickly. 'How soon do you want things moving?'

'Yesterday?' The black brows rose quizzically. 'It's a priority, I'm afraid. I don't know what else you've got on, but if you take this job I would expect everything else to come second.'

Yes, I can see you would expect that, she thought testily. But she kept her face blank before forcing a smile as she said, 'No problem. Because of the language aspect I would be doing the initial groundwork, and Russell can cope with the work we have at present. We're used to working at quite a hectic pace; that's what marketing is all about.'

As the waiter removed their plates Colt nodded before saying, 'Liqueur coffee? Claude does the best one in London.'

'Just black, please; I'm too full for anything else.' The champagne cocktail had been followed by a glass of wine with the meal, and although she felt perfectly sober she wasn't risking anything but the clearest head around Colt Irons.

'Two black coffees, please,' he said pleasantly to the waiter, who bobbed his head in acknowledgement before gliding away, and the thought struck her, as it had done once or twice during the evening, that he was surprisingly warm and civil to the staff. She had been in the company of men with far less wealth and influence than Colt Irons who considered waiters as menials who were less than dust under their feet. But there was none of that arrogance with Colt.

He was a strange man… And unsettling—*very* unsettling. It bothered her more than she could say that she was mean-minded enough to wish he were churlish and pretentious so she could have reason to despise him. Oh, she was horrible. What on earth was the matter with her tonight, anyway?

'Did you know Harry and Carol are seeing each other?' he asked with that suddenness she was getting used to.

'Yes.' Her voice was hesitant, reluctant. She had spoken to her cousin once or twice on the phone since the weekend in Brindale, and the developing relationship with Lord Brindale's youngest son worried her. She didn't want Carol to get hurt, especially after the pain she had suffered at the hands of Robert Stanton, and Carol was so warm, so giving; she had no hard shell to protect her from the darts of life.

'Don't sound too thrilled for her,' he said now, with a mocking coldness that made anger flare briefly before she acknowledged he had no idea where she was coming from.

'I am pleased for Carol,' she said tightly, 'if Harry Brindale is genuine—otherwise she'll be hurt, and badly. She…she's just had one long-term relationship that ended badly; I don't want the same thing to happen again.'

'That's up to Carol, surely?' He settled back in his

seat as the waiter brought the coffee but as soon as he'd gone Colt said, 'I'm glad there seems to be at least one member of your family who has the courage to follow her heart.'

'Meaning?' she asked icily, knowing quite well what he was insinuating.

'Meaning I gather you haven't taken my tried and tested advice,' he returned, with a cool disapproval that made her want to forget she was a sophisticated career woman having dinner with an influential prospective client and stick her tongue out at him as far as it would reach—just to see the shock on that irritatingly superior face at such childish defiance.

She didn't doubt that he was deferred to like a little tin god in his own domain, or that any insubordination or rebelliousness by lesser mortals would be dealt with swiftly and ruthlessly. Well, she could handle that—just—when it pertained to work matters, but this was something quite different and he might as well know now that she would brook no interference in her private life, however lucrative the job might prove.

'I think you'll find the dictionary definition of advice is a given opinion,' she said coldly. 'I respect the fact you have your own opinions on matters, apparently one of which is my love life—'

'Or lack of it,' he interrupted expressionlessly.

'Or lack of it,' she repeated frostily. 'But it so happens I have a mind of my own too, and I think in this case at least my judgement is based on more substantial grounds than yours.'

'Rubbish.' It was said entirely without rancour and was all the more annoying because of it. 'You're following the ostrich syndrome—bury your head in the sand and it'll all go away. But it won't, you know.' He watched her increasingly angry face with cool grey eyes. 'You're going to have to jump in the deep end again sooner or later, and with your looks and body it should be sooner—'

'Well! Really—' But he swept on regardless of her rage.

'And I'm not being insulting so don't glare at me like that, woman. Can't you see all this hiding away is doing you no good? You won't get over William like that—believe me, I know. Have some fun for a time; forget the past and concentrate on the present—nothing heavy, just fun.' A black eyebrow raised itself quizzically.

'I don't want to have fun,' she ground out through clenched teeth. 'I want—'

'To pine away from unrequited love. Well, you've done that for six months and that's quite long enough. He doesn't deserve six days' worth of tears let alone six months, Jessica. You must be able to see that, surely?' His dark head tilted to one side as he surveyed her pitilessly with narrowed eyes. 'Well, you're an intelligent woman. You can see it, can't you?' he persisted scathingly.

'You're…you're horrible.' She wasn't going to cry—*no way* was she going to cry, she told herself furiously as her cheeks burnt hotly.

'No, just practical.' If she had been looking at his face at that moment she would have seen the firmness of his mouth soften with a touch of compassion, but her eyes were tight on her hands clasped in her lap and the moment passed.

'And this…practicality extends to Jo too, I suppose?' she said with bitter resentment, raising blazing eyes to his now expressionless face. 'What are you suggesting? That I should give her a ring and say, Thanks for stealing my fiancé and sleeping with him for months behind my back—can I be godmother to the baby when it's born? How am I? Oh, I'm fine, Jo; I'm having fun, fun, fun…?'

'It was a filthy trick and if you never forgive her until the day you die it's exactly what she deserves.' The darkness in his voice cut through her rage like a knife through butter, and there was something in the deadly rawness that told her he wasn't just speaking about

William and Jo. There was something…something more…

'But that's a thing apart. I'm not saying you have to forgive them, Jessica, any of them. In fact what you're feeling now will motivate you on and up if you harness it correctly.' He *was* talking about himself, she thought dazedly, her eyes remaining riveted on the handsome, cold face in front of her. 'Know yourself—your weaknesses, your strengths, your failures, all of it. Through something like this you can really know yourself and then you're a formidable opponent.'

'But perhaps I don't want to be a formidable opponent,' she whispered weakly. 'And I would have thought the sort of self-knowledge you're talking about is a dangerous thing.'

'Why?' The magnetic, captivating side of his personality had never seemed so marked as he leant towards her now, his eyes glittering with grey light and his gaze intent. 'Why dangerous?'

'It's something I read once,' she answered slowly. 'I can't quite remember where. But the writer was saying that with complete self-knowledge there is no uncertainty, no doubt—'

'And that's bad?' he asked derisively, with mocking contempt.

'If it dehumanises, yes.' Her eyes were steady now, holding his—in which she saw, just for a fleeting second, an expression of what she thought was shock before the cold grey depths iced over.

'I'm human, Jessica.' He reached across the table and took her hand and his flesh was warm on hers, creating a shiver of reaction she found impossible to hide. 'I'm very human.' His voice was caressing and deep, its tone one she hadn't heard before, and which sent flickers of something hot into every nerve and sinew before they culminated in her lower stomach in an ache that was physically intoxicating.

'Don't...' But her whisper was a plea he chose to ignore.

'And humans need to touch, to taste, to explore...don't they?' The words in themselves could have meant anything but his eyes were on her mouth now, softly, luxuriously almost, stroking over the moist, full contours of her lips until she had to cool their heat with the tip of her tongue, an action that brought dark satisfaction to the slate-grey gaze. 'Don't they?' he asked again, his voice soft.

'I...I don't know.' This was crazy, indecent. He couldn't be making love to her in the middle of a crowded restaurant, could he? But that was exactly what it felt like and one thing was for sure—William had never made her feel like this in the whole of their time together...

'No?' The spiralling whirlwind of bitter-sweet sensation was out of control now, her whole world narrowed down to the dark, handsome face opposite her. 'Then let me show you, my little wench; let me show you what you should command, *expect*—your right as a beautiful woman who was born to be appreciated and adored.'

'What...what are you saying?' she asked breathlessly, weak confusion evident in every line of her face and body.

'I want you, Jessica,' he said softly. 'I want you very badly, more than I've wanted anyone in a long, long time.'

She shuddered, unable to take the mental step backwards, that she knew was imperative, vital. 'You don't mean that.'

'I do.' He smiled slowly, his face overwhelming in its male strength and confidence. 'I'm what you need right now; I know it. We'd be good together. You aren't looking for any messy entanglements any more than I am; you need to relax and have fun with the knowledge that there are no ties, no commitment. Carol told Harry you're determined to concentrate on your career for the next decade or so, to build yourself a reputation and carve out some street cred—and that's fine; I like that. I could help you, Jessica. Smooth the way.'

And then she understood, really understood, and with the understanding came flat, hard reality like a bucket of cold water poured over her head. He was offering her an affair, a physical partaking of each other's bodies, that was all. Maybe some sort of friendship—*maybe*—certainly the promise that he would oil the wheels of her career—perhaps act as her mentor once he had tired of her body, even? But it was all a cold-blooded logical proposition to him—he wanted her and so he intended to buy her. Simple.

But oh, no, Mr Irons, she thought tightly, white-hot rage and disappointment bringing her small chin up and out, not so simple! In this instance, at least, satisfaction is not guaranteed in spite of your wealth and power. Sorry, Russell…

'I think I understand, Mr Irons,' she said with cutting contempt as she rose slowly to stand looking down at his surprised face, her own as white as a sheet with two spots of colour burning on her cheekbones. 'And I'm sorry, but you've wasted a perfectly good dinner. I have no intention of sleeping with you to get the Scotland job or any other. So I suggest you go and find one of those obliging females you mentioned earlier, who I'm sure will be only too grateful to share your bed. I'll take it as read you'll be looking for another firm to market your project. Goodnight.'

She had moved past him and out of range before he had time to speak, the look of stunned amazement on his face going some way to counter the deep, mortifying humiliation she was feeling. And she almost ran across the restaurant and out through the door without looking to left or right, bursting into the London night as though the devil himself were after her.

CHAPTER FOUR

'JESSICA!' Her name was a snarl and as she felt herself being whirled round by a steel-hard hand on her arm no power on earth could have prevented her from striking out with all the strength she possessed. She felt her hand connect with the taut, firm skin of Colt's face in a resounding blow, the sound of which actually echoed in the quiet London street. But then both arms were being held in a vice-like grip that rendered her helpless in spite of her struggles. He was swearing profusely, his face black with rage as he attempted to restrain her without causing her physical harm, and when at last her strength was gone they were both panting as though they had been in a race.

'Are you mad, woman? Are you?' She tried to pull away from him but it was only a token gesture and they both knew it. She was shaking so badly she could barely stand. 'I've met some wildcats in my time but you sure as hell take the biscuit.'

'You mean I ought to be grateful for your disgusting proposition?'

'What proposition, for crying out loud? I merely suggested we could see a little of each other, that's all—'

'You did not!' she snapped furiously. 'You know only too well what you were implying. I'm not that stupid—'

'"Stupid" is far too mild a word to describe you, I do agree.' A big black limousine turned the corner and cruised down the street and he thrust her forward none too gently. 'Come on; I've no intention of discussing this in the street,' he said tightly.

'Take your hands off me, Colt Irons.' She tried to jerk free but his hands were unrelenting. 'I mean it; I'm not going anywhere with you.'

'Give me strength…' He shut his eyes for one angry moment, and then she found herself being hauled towards the Ferrari before she could say another word and unceremoniously propelled into the beautiful interior. 'You dare, you just *dare* to try and leave and I swear I'll put you over my knee and spank some sense into you right here in the street,' he ground out through gritted teeth, staring down at her before slamming the passenger door shut.

'You wouldn't!' She was into the attack as soon as he slid into the driver's seat. 'Not even you would behave like that.'

'Try me.' His voice was very soft but with all the flexibility of cold steel and as he turned to look at her she saw his eyes were glittering with an unholy rage. 'I never say anything I don't mean, Jessica, nor do I make threats I'm not prepared to carry out. Now I don't know exactly what you've heard about me to inspire such dislike and mistrust, or from whom, but this is straight from the horse's mouth so you can take it as a dead cert— you are going to sit and listen to what I have to say or you won't be able to sit comfortably for a week.'

She tried to drag the tattered remains of her composure about her before saying weakly, 'You're a bully.'

'And worse, much worse, so just pray you won't find out how low I can sink,' he said with scathing mockery.

'I don't believe you're behaving like this.' She wanted her tone to match his but it merely sounded breathless.

'*You* don't believe *I'm* behaving like this?' he asked with unfeigned amazement, before shaking his head with what looked suspiciously like wonder. 'Now I really have heard it all…'

She was about to argue some more when her gaze fell on the vivid red handprint outlining one side of his face, and suddenly her speech process came to an abrupt halt. She'd hit him—him—Colt Irons—and not just a tap either. Oh, hell… Now it was she who shut her eyes for a moment. She'd never behaved like this before in her life, not even in the midst of the misery and humiliation of her wedding day. What was it about this man that brought out the very worst in her? But to hit him—she must be cracking up...

'Are you going to listen to me, Jessica?' His voice was quiet now but with a layer of frost that made it crackle.

'Yes.' She couldn't bring herself to look at him, staring down at her hands clasped in her lap, her cheeks feeling as though they were on fire. What a night. It was even worse than the one a few weeks ago at the Brindales' and she'd thought that would take some beating.

'Now quite why I'm bothering to explain myself I don't know.' Again there was that element of surprise in the dark male voice and she glanced at him quickly before lowering her gaze again. He looked mad. Oh, he did look mad. 'I should kick you out of this car and let you find your own way home.'

'That's fine by me.'

As she made to move his voice lashed out with all the latent fury she'd suspected he was holding in check. '*Sit still!*' She sat.

He took a long, deep breath before raking his hand through his hair and thrusting his big body back against the seat in a gesture that spoke of intense irritation. 'You'd need the patience of Job,' he muttered irascibly.

'What?' She had heard him but thought it prudent to pretend otherwise.

'Nothing.' He turned to her and when he spoke her name his voice was perfectly under control.

'Jessica, my...proposal, if you want to call it that, was an invitation—not a threat. I had no intention of implying it was obligatory to share my bed. I merely thought, in view of recent events, that you might be ready to start enjoying life again and I thought we saw eye to eye on the ''no strings attached'' aspect. Now...' He paused but she still kept her gaze on her hands. 'Do you believe me?'

Did she believe him? Her thoughts were racing but one thing was perfectly clear: *no, she darn well didn't*, and she was blowed if she was going to play this particular game. She had come through the searing humiliation and pain of the last few months, albeit crawling inch by anguished inch, and if there was one thing she had learnt in it all it was that she was never, ever going to be taken for a ride by any man again. She would demand honesty in any relationship in the future—stark, naked honesty of the most searching kind—and if she demanded it it was only right she played by her own rules. It would be easy to pretend, to smooth things over, to soothe the bruised ego, but she admitted, 'No, I don't believe you, Colt.'

There was absolute silence for a moment and then she raised her head and stared straight into the handsome, cold face.

'I see.' His voice was quite expressionless.

'No, I don't think you do.' She forced herself to go on. 'I don't know what sort of women you are used to dealing with, and before you say it I'm aware it's none of my business anyway, but the way you spoke in there was cut and dried. You were outlining the advantages of my having an affair with you, it's as simple as that, whether you intended to or not. Perhaps the women in your world would appreciate such a straightforward, businesslike approach, but—'

'You don't,' he finished for her, his voice deep and flat.

'No, I don't.' There was no apology in her tone. 'I find it…unsavoury.'

'Unsavoury!' There was plenty of expression in his voice now.

'Added to which I don't sleep around,' she stated unflinchingly. He might as well get it all in one fell swoop; she'd well and truly blown the job now anyway. 'Not before and not now.'

'I never imagined you did,' he said tightly.

He smelt wonderful. She didn't know where the thought came from, and in the circumstances she could well have done without it, but in the close confines of the car the faint lemony smell from his hair mingling with the musky aftershave she remembered so well was doing incredible things to her hormones.

But that was part of it all, wasn't it? she told herself warningly. The seduction technique, the enticing magnetism of the man. Oh, yes, he had it all and he knew it. She felt a moment's very real regret that she couldn't be the sort of woman he wanted and that shocked her into speech more effectively than anything else could have done. 'I'd like to leave now.'

In the same second that her hand reached for the car door his voice froze the movement. 'Sit still, damn you.'

'I've said all I want to say,' she said carefully, darting one quick glance at his dark face before looking away.

'Good for you.' The mockery was biting. 'But now it's my turn. I get the impression you imagine I operate my love life like a number twenty-one bus; is that right? Passenger gets on board, enjoys the ride, alights at the appropriate stop to make room for my next fare, yes? Something along those lines?'

Why, oh, why hadn't she just said she believed him and got him to take her home? she asked herself silently. This honesty thing was all very well but perhaps it would have been better to start it when he wasn't quite so close.

'Well?' His voice was as cold as ice and the tone was such that it brought her head jerking up.

'I wouldn't have put it quite like that,' she said tightly. 'But by your own admission you have lots of women you could call if you wanted—I mean, you said there were women...' She was floundering and the cruel mouth twisted mockingly.

'I know what I said, Jessica.' He continued to hold

her glance for one more moment before settling back in his seat with an irritable sigh as he stared out of the windscreen. 'And it's true, in its own way. I'm a very wealthy man, and single—' he flashed one searing glance at her from glittering grey eyes '—which proves a fatal combination to some females...those of the more...predatory variety. There will always be women who find wealth and power a heady aphrodisiac, who are prepared to offer all in the hope of conquest—'

'And you approve of that?' she asked hotly.

'Of course I don't.' His voice had been a bark and he moderated the pitch as he continued, 'But it's a fact of life and one which it would be foolish to ignore. It's true there are women who make it plain I only have to lift up the phone and they'll be there, but such forwardness does not appeal to me. Whether you believe that or not is of no consequence. My...relationships have always been conducted with women I can respect and like and who, I hope, respect and like me in return. And no, there has not been a steady stream, before you ask.'

'I wouldn't dream of asking,' she said stiffly.

'No? You surprise me.' His voice was very dry. 'I am not promiscuous, Jessica, but neither have I got to the age of thirty-five without some sexual encounters along the way. The fact that the newspapers take great delight in reporting if I so much as smile at a woman has rather enhanced my sexual prowess with both the media and the public at large, but there is nothing I can do about that. My close friends and family know the truth, and that is all that concerns me.'

His family? It was ridiculous, but she hadn't imagined him having any kith and kin—he was the epitome of the wolf that walked alone—but of course he would have relations, people he was close to. What would it be like to be part of his family, to be able to claim some tentative link, a bond? 'You said back there in the restaurant you don't want any ties,' she said carefully. 'Didn't you?'

'Yes.' The one word was not encouraging but she continued anyway.

'Then that means your relationships are started on the understanding they won't be permanent, press or no press.' The hard grey gaze switched from the windscreen to her face and she felt the impact down to her toes. 'You were talking about our having fun which roughly translates means sex along with, I'm sure, several nice dinners and outings and—'

'All right, all right, you've made your point,' he bit out savagely, dull red colour searing the harsh cheekbones.

'I'm sorry, Colt, but I don't like that,' she said tightly. 'You were trying to buy me and you haven't got the guts to admit it. Now we could sit here all night discussing it but I shan't change my mind—'

'How very moral of you.' She didn't recognise the thread of self-contempt in his voice. All she heard was the very real resentment and exasperation that coloured the deep tones with black ice, so when, in the next moment, he moved across his seat and took her in his arms she couldn't have been more surprised.

The kiss was hard but not brutal, his mouth taking possession of hers with an innate mastery that brought her senses leaping to instant and glorious life, and she just didn't have the sexual experience to be able to hide what he was doing to her as her limbs turned liquid.

His hands slid down her silk-covered arms, his thumbs just touching the soft swell of her breasts, which responded with an immediate and traitorous tightening as he pulled her against the hard wall of his chest. And as her lips opened in a little gasp of disbelief at what his body was doing to hers his tongue penetrated the moist contours beyond with devasting provocativeness. The kiss was thorough and passionately intent, sensitising every nerve-end and sending the blood rushing through her veins with a sensual warmth that increased the alien ache in her most intimate places until she was trembling helplessly against the hard planes of his body.

And then he moved—lazily, almost casually settling back into his own seat, from where he surveyed her flushed, stunned face with narrowed grey eyes. 'You're sure you won't change your mind?' he asked softly, his voice a caress in itself. 'I can promise you you won't have to lie back and think of England, if that's what's worrying you.'

It was said mockingly—he was all too well aware of the effect his lovemaking had produced—and it hurt—badly. He was playing with her, she thought painfully, amusing himself at her expense, quite confident in his ability to break down her defences and subjugate her to his will. No doubt it was something of a novelty to have to try and persuade a woman into his bed. From what she had heard they normally were all too willing to race him under the covers.

Well, she was no little toy or trinket to amuse the world-weary mind and body of Colt Irons. He could look elsewhere for his diversions. The thought took shape and solidified—and with it her anger. 'I didn't think for a moment I would,' she said coldly, her voice shaking with rage rather than desire as white-hot fury wiped away all traces of his sensual touch. 'But I want more than a performance in bed, amazing though it may seem to you. Trust, faithfulness—love; I prefer those things to a ten out of ten score.'

His body had stiffened as she had spoken, the smiling mockery wiped from his face like magic. 'And that was what your fiancé gave you, was it?' he asked with acid cruelty. 'While he was sleeping with your sister? At least I'm being honest—

'I'm sorry.' When she reached for the door handle his hand came across hers as he leant across her seat. 'That was unforgivable.'

'Yes, it was,' she said shakily, forcing speech through stiff lips. 'And stupid and shallow…' She raised her

head and looked straight into his face, her eyes glittering
with unshed tears. 'I'm not responsible for what William
did, but just because he betrayed everything he was it
doesn't mean I have to do the same. I won't become like
him…or you.'

'You're comparing me with him?' In another world,
at another time, his enraged incredulity would have been
amusing but right now it merely brought her head up
still further.

'Too true.' She glared at him, aware she had hit him
on the raw and fiercely glad of it. It was weak conso-
lation after his cutting cruelty, but better than nothing.

He opened his mouth to reply, stared at her white face
for a long moment before biting back what was obviously another assault on her fragile equilibrium and then
flung himself fully into his seat, starting the engine with
a savage movement that threatened to break the key in
the ignition.

The drive back to her bedsit was conducted in absolute silence, the atmosphere so icy, Jessica wouldn't
have been surprised if the air had shattered around them.
Colt drove with a deadly ferocity that had her home in
half the time it had taken for them to reach the restaurant, and as he drew up outside the house she was out
of the car before he could open his door—still without
speaking a word.

She thought she heard him call her name as she sped
up the steps, but she didn't stop in her headlong dash,
opening the door and almost falling into the house and
not really feeling safe until she was in her own little
bedsit with the door locked and bolted. She stood for
some minutes leaning against the hard wood, her heart
pounding but her mind curiously numb as she fought to
bring her trembling under control. And then she walked
across the room, sinking down into a chair and shutting
her eyes as she let her limbs go limp.

'He's a monster…' The murmur was almost inaudible
but it triggered her thinking again, and as a mixture of

humiliation, embarrassment and sheer rage brought her to her feet she kicked off her shoes before almost tearing the dress off her body. It was as she flung it to the floor, in a gesture that repudiated utterly the events of the evening, that the corsage scattered its velvet petals in a whirling arc of white, like confetti at a wedding, releasing the dam of tears that she had been keeping at bay.

CHAPTER FIVE

How was she going to tell him? As Jessica raced up the steps of the office building in which Russell rented his business premises her heart was in her mouth. Not only was she nearly an hour late, for the first time ever, but she was going to have to admit to her boss that she had effectively blown the biggest contract they had had the chance of for a long time. And both lapses of grace were down to the same cause—Colt Irons.

Dawn had been breaking by the time she had fallen into a troubled doze, its pale pink fingers creeping across the night sky that she had been observing through the dark hours as her mind had sought peace. And when she'd awoken with a frantic start at just after nine it was to the knowledge that she had completely forgotten to set her alarm the night before.

Her hasty toilet completed, she had flown out of the house and hailed a taxi, a luxury she rarely indulged in, and had sat rehearsing her apologies for the whole of the journey before admitting to herself that Russell wasn't going to listen to her side of things at all. He would be livid...

Mandy, the receptionist, raised her blonde head as Jessica walked towards the lift with a customary 'good morning'. 'Oh, hi...' she drawled uninterestedly, before her gaze narrowed on Jessica's pale face and pink-rimmed eyes. 'You look terrible; aren't you well?' she asked, with a touch more attention.

'Just a summer cold,' Jessica lied cheerfully, giving a loud sniff to emphasise the point.

'Oh, right...' Mandy's voice trailed off as her eyes dropped to the nail she had been painting when Jessica had walked in, and Jessica heaved a sigh of relief as she stepped into the lift. Social chit-chat was definitely not on the agenda this morning.

Once the lift had deposited her on the fifth floor she stood for a moment in the deserted corridor, the sounds of activity filtering through from behind closed doors. She'd better get it over with, she thought despondently, taking a long, hard breath before walking to the far end where Russell's rooms were situated. He wasn't going to like it, she knew that, but even Russell's driving ambition wouldn't countenance her sleeping with a client in order to secure a contract...would it? Well, if it would perhaps she'd be better off in another job anyway...

She nodded to herself before opening the door into the large outer office, Russell having a tiny office off the main room which he rarely used, preferring to work with his staff.

Susan, the typist and general dogsbody, gave her a wide smile as she walked in. 'When it got to half past nine I was expecting a call to say you were ill,' she said by way of a greeting. 'Everything all right?'

'Overslept,'' Jessica returned briefly. 'Russell in his office?'

But before the other girl could reply Russell's door opened to reveal his portly frame in the doorway, a beaming smile on his face. 'Who's a clever girl, then?'

'I don't know; who is?' Jessica asked weakly. This wasn't at all what she had expected and it was going to make the telling harder.

'I had a call from Colt Irons at five past nine this morning—'

'I can explain everything,' Jessica began, but Russell continued as though she hadn't spoken.

'To say we've got the contract.' His smile expanded from ear to ear. 'He wants you to deal with the European side first, get that moving; the other can wait. He's away for a week or two now but he wants some results by the time he gets back. Now, clear your desk and we'll sort out what's what. There's a great pile of literature on my desk that one of his assistants dropped in a few minutes ago—you'll have to sift through that first.'

He didn't give her a chance to speak, which was just as well. All coherent thought had left her head, and it was some minutes before she realised she was working on automatic without hearing a word Russell was saying.

Pull yourself together, Jessica; this really won't do, she told herself vehemently as she gazed vacantly into Russell's animated face, watching his lips without the sound registering in her brain at all. The ringing of the telephone saved the day, but then her face froze as Susan called across to her, her hand over the mouthpiece.

'Jess? It's Colt Irons. Are you free to talk to him?'

'Are you mad, girl?' Russell's growl had Susan blinking at him. 'Of course she's free; it's Colt Irons.' It was said with the reverence accorded to royalty and as Jessica picked up her phone she couldn't help thinking that Russell would have made a perfect diplomat, his sense of adroit diplomacy combining with an air of ingratiating homage that would appeal to some of the inflated egos they dealt with fairly regularly.

But not Colt Irons. The thought was intrusive and unwelcome. He'd see right through any obsequiousness and go straight for the jugular.

'Jessica?' The deep, husky voice was clearly impatient. 'You've spoken to Russell?'

'I… Yes.' She hated the breathless note in her voice.

'It's no strings attached; you understand me?' he asked coldly. 'I want a good job done and I think you're the person to do it. I'm away for a while, but I've put my PA, Jack Goode, fully in the picture so if you need to liaise with anyone give him a ring. I'd like approximate figures, contacts et cetera on my desk by the twentieth, okay?'

'I—'

'Goodbye, Jessica.' And the phone went down with an abruptness that made her wince. Oh, she loathed him, job or no job. He had to be the most arrogant, over-bearing…

'Well?' Russell was hovering at her side like an over-anxious parent on the first day of school. 'What was that about? Is everything all right? What did he say?'

'He wants facts and figures by the twentieth,' Jessica said briefly, 'and he's given me the name of his PA to liaise with. That gives me—' she consulted her calendar '—just over two weeks, so I'd better get cracking.'

The next two weeks passed in a haze of work, work and more work, but at the end of it Jessica had everything that was needed for the next stage of the project, albeit at the cost of three or four hours' sleep a night. But she would have walked through coals of fire, swum naked in shark-infested seas, *anything* to deliver the goods, she thought fiercely as she travelled to Colt's main offices in Tilbury with Russell on the twentieth of July. It had become a matter of supreme importance to impress Colt Irons with her business acumen, although she didn't venture to ask herself why. It didn't occur to her that she hadn't given William and Jo more than a passing thought in the last two weeks either.

All her being, every nerve and vein, was concentrated on the impending meeting and she was as tense as a coiled spring as they walked into a massive high room with a huge plate-glass window that took in a sweep of sky and land that was stunning. It was Colt's own private office.

'Jessica?' Jack Goode, a tall, good-looking man in his late twenties, held out his hand just as Colt walked through from an adjoining room. 'It's so nice to put a face to the voice, although I have to say the face has exceeded all my expectations.'

She smiled at him warmly; he had been of enormous help over the last two weeks with the hundreds of tiny details she had needed to liaise on. Now her voice re-flected her gratitude as she said, 'Likewise, Jack,' before turning to face the big dark figure that had occupied her days and her nights, if only half her dreams were remembered, for weeks.

'Good morning, Colt.' If anyone else noticed the change in her voice as she addressed him they were too polite to let it show, but the devastating grey gaze that had the power to slice through solid steel was icy as he inclined his head her way.

'Jessica.' The deep voice was coldly polite. 'Russell. Do sit down; we have a lot to get through in the next little while.'

It set the tone for the morning. There were no smiles, no light chit-chat to alleviate the pressure. Colt had determined the pace and they all had to dance to his tune, Jessica thought militantly as the hours sped by. He was an egotistical, arrogant swine of a man, that was what he was. But why did he have to be so incredibly fascinating too? And he was—oh, he was. Everything about him, every little gesture and movement of his body, proclaimed power and authority and a sensuality that was frightening.

'You've done an excellent job, Jessica; thank you.' The accolade was unexpected and, if the faces of Colt's own personnel were anything to go by, unusual. 'Unfortunately I should have been somewhere else half an hour ago,' Colt continued as he turned to Russell. 'But lunch is waiting for you in the executive dining room. My secretary will take you along there.'

'No problem, I can do that,' Jack Goode interjected hastily, with a sidelong glance at Jessica that Colt didn't miss.

'I think not.' Colt's voice was a study in neutrality. 'I need you with me, Jack.'

'Oh, but I thought—'

'Change of plan.' Colt's voice was pleasant but there was something running underneath that was lethal. 'Pick up the McLain file from Accounts, would you, and I'll see you in the car park?'

'Right.' Jack clearly didn't have a clue what was going on but just as clearly wasn't going to argue with his chairman and managing director. 'It's been nice meeting you.' His smile was polite with Russell but rose several degrees when he turned to Jessica, bringing a tinge of pink to her cheeks.

'Thank you for all your help.' Jessica smiled back, her voice warm. 'I'll be in touch about that French set-up within the week. I rather think Mr Dupont is going to insist on a meeting.'

'No problem.' Jack's eyes crinkled at the corners as he shook her hand, holding her fingers just a second longer than was necessary before nodding again at Russell as he left the room.

'Nice young man.' Russell's voice was a shade patronising as he turned to Colt, indicating that he considered himself on a higher plane than the young personal assistant, although there was certainly no justification for such a belief.

Colt's voice reflected this as he coolly stated, 'First-class qualifications and an excellent mind to boot. Jack Goode is already a force to be reckoned with within the business world, which is why I prefer him working for me than for any of the opposition.'

'Yes, of course.' Russell recognised he had been put in his place by an expert and was wise enough to say nothing more as they all left the room, walking through into the secretary's office where a stunning creature, who looked as if she had just stepped straight out of a top-class fashion magazine, was working with incredible speed at a word processor.

'Danielle, would you show my guests to the executive dining room, please?' Colt said pleasantly as the brunette raised beautiful blue eyes to meet his. 'Jack was going to be host but something has cropped up, so if you wouldn't mind taking an early lunch...?'

'Of course, Mr Irons.' The exquisitely painted mouth gave an air-hostess smile that spoke of utter aplomb and

control. 'If you'd like to come this way?' Her glance
included them both but there was no warmth in the perfect features.

'Goodbye.' Just before she followed the other two
Jessica held out her hand to Colt, with the polite smile
she had practised for days in front of the mirror stitched
on her face.

'Goodbye, Jessica.' His voice was soft and deep as he
spoke her name, as different from the cold, abrupt tone
he had used all morning as it was possible for it to be.
He smiled at her slowly, the dark grey eyes piercingly
intent on her face. 'I think we'll have all this tied up
within a couple of weeks, don't you?' he asked quietly.

'What? Oh, yes; yes, I'm sure we will.' She was gab-
bling, and she heard herself with a burst of self-
contempt, but with her fingers buried in his and the smell
and feel of him all around it was hard to keep in smart
career mode.

The other two were out of sight in the corridor and
as she made a gesture to join them his hand tightened
on hers before he turned her fingers over in his, exposing
her small pink palm. 'Till then...' He bent his head, his
lips fastening on the centre of the delicate flesh, and she
felt the impact like a bolt of lightning right down to her
toes, causing her to pull her hand away with a gasp of
shock, and thrust it behind her back.

'Don't.' She stared at him, her eyes enormous as she
tried to control the shivers of reaction his touch had induced.

'Why? Because you like it?' he asked silkily, his dark
face enigmatic and closed.

'I...I'm here to do a job—'

'Which you are accomplishing beautifully,' he said
with complete seriousness.

'I work for you, that's all.' She wanted her voice to
be firm and composed but the trembling whisper in no
way matched the desire.

'Yes, for the moment you work for me, Jessica,' he

agreed softly, the grey eyes dark and unfathomable as he drew a veil over their expression. 'But one day soon the job will be finished.'

'I... They're waiting for me.' She backed away from him, her gaze still fastened on his face as though she were retreating from a dangerous animal, and now the hard male features iced over as she fairly scrambled through the doorway with a muttered 'Goodbye.'

Oh, was she destined to forever make a fool of herself in front of this man? Jessica asked herself as she followed the other two into the lift. What must he think? She resisted the impulse to press her fingers tight over her eyeballs as she considered her undignified rush from the room. Here he was, surrounded by the sort of breathtaking, elegant sophisticates his secretary represented, both in work and out, and all he had done was kiss her hand as she had left. And what had she done? Leapt away like a scalded cat and turned to jelly.

She wanted to moan and clench her fists together but forced herself to stand quietly as she listened to Russell trying to charm Danielle. No doubt Colt's usual women would have had a light, charming remark ready to hand and the whole incident would have been beneficial to both—a cultured, subtle exchange between sexes that was both cosmopolitan and refined. And what had she said? 'Don't.' *Don't.* She must have made some sound because both Russell and Danielle turned to her, the former's eyes enquiring and the latter's cool and blank.

'Did you say something?' Russell asked, his gaze narrowing on her hot cheeks.

'I... No, it's just a little too warm.' She managed a weak smile. 'I'm feeling a bit odd; I shall be better when I've had lunch.'

'Do you eat breakfast?' Danielle asked, a spark of interest in her voice for the first time.

'I didn't this morning.' She had been too nervous at the thought of seeing Colt again to manage more than two fortifying cups of black coffee first thing.

'Oh, but you must. I always have two slices of crisp-bread and a bowl of sliced grapefruit for breakfast,' Danielle said with the intensity of a veteran slimmer, a fact that was subsequently substantiated as Colt's secretary persisted in detailing her eating habits on and off all through lunch while she nibbled daintily at a plain green salad.

'How long have you worked for Colt?' Russell asked at the end of a long exposition on the attributes of plenty of fibre, the faintly desperate note in his voice indicating that his initial interest in the beautiful brunette had long since vanished.

'Nine years, since leaving university.' The animation had gone from Danielle's voice now food was off the agenda.

'You must know him very well.' Russell smiled encouragingly but Jessica suspected he wasn't so much being nosy as delaying the inevitable return to Danielle's favourite subject.

'As well as anyone. Mr Irons is not a man one can get close to—not since the accident, anyway.'

'The accident?' Now it was Jessica who pricked up her ears. 'He was involved in an accident?'

'Not personally, no.' Danielle's vivid blue eyes drifted over Jessica's face. 'His fiancée and sister were killed in a car accident just a few months after I came to work for him. Of course he wasn't so wealthy then, only just starting out, I guess. But the rest is history, as they say.'

'He's done very well.' As Russell continued the conversation Jessica found she had lost her appetite. He had been engaged to be married? He had loved someone enough to ask them to spend the rest of their life with him? And then she had been taken from him, his sister too, in one of the bizarre twists of fate that life loved to play. How had he taken it? She shook herself mentally as she told herself not to be so stupid. She *knew* how he had taken it; the man he was now was proof of how hard the blow had hit.

She sat amidst the discreet, quiet murmur of the executive dining room as the conversation dipped and swayed around her, her thoughts racing. What exactly had happened? Had there been another car involved? Where had he been? Who had been driving?

'Who was driving?' She wasn't aware she had spoken her thoughts out loud until Russell and Danielle turned to her with surprised faces as she cut into their conversation.

'I'm sorry?' Danielle wrinkled her perfect brow.

'When Colt's fiancée and sister were killed. Who was driving?' Jessica repeated urgently.

'I really don't remember.' Danielle looked at her as though she had taken leave of her senses. 'His sister, I think. Why?'

'If you never forgive her until the day you die it's exactly what she deserves.' The words, and the frightening darkness in his face as he had spoken them, were stark and clear in front of her. It had been *his* sister he'd been talking about, she thought, horror-stricken, not hers. All the rage and resentment and terrifying bitterness she had sensed in that moment some weeks ago had been real, but directed at his sister—not Jo.

Did he hate his own flesh and blood so completely because she had been the means of destroying the woman he loved? But that was awful, terrible. Whatever the circumstances of the accident, if his sister had died too she had paid the ultimate price. Surely that alone would instigate some feelings of exoneration?

She sat in silence for the rest of the meal, letting the other two carry the conversation, her mind dissecting the few facts she had been given. She didn't understand the first thing about this man...and she wanted to. As the thought struck her the danger signals went off, hot and strong. It was utter foolishness. In view of all he had said, perhaps emotional suicide would be a better description, she thought wryly, but she wanted to understand what made Colt Irons tick.

There was much more to this man than met the eye; she knew it. But how did one begin to penetrate a barrier of steel? One didn't. The answer was cold and final, but she recognised it as fact. She had to get on with the job she had been given, deliver the goods, and then run like hell—from him, and her own dangerous weakness where he was concerned. She didn't have the experience or the worldly wisdom needed to begin a relationship with someone like Colt—he would eat her up and spit her out and not even notice.

The greyness that settled on her at that moment didn't lift all day, continuing through the frantic afternoon right up until the moment she left the office to find a low, sleek Ferrari parked on double yellow lines right outside the office block. 'Colt?' She stopped at the top of the steps, staring down at the long, lean individual draped against the car bonnet.

'Hi.' His smile was lazy and cool, and suddenly the sky was bluer, the fume-laden air sweeter, the whole evening taking on a magical glow.

Steady, girl, steady. All the hard talking she had done to herself through lunch rushed through her mind but with Colt right in front of her it lost its punch. Nevertheless, she managed to retain some degree of composure instead of melting on the spot, forcing a light smile before she said, 'Problems?' He must have called with some difficulty regarding the project; she'd be foolish to think anything else, she told herself as her heart thudded against her breastbone.

'A killer.' His eyes were tight on her face as she walked down the steps, and the knowledge that that discerning gaze would pick up any show of emotion kept her from revealing the sharp stab of disappointment that had pierced her heart at his words. Of course it was a work problem—she'd known that, hadn't she? she berated herself silently as she kept the smile in place by sheer will-power. And that was good, perfect. She didn't need anything else.

'How can I help?' As she reached the car he levered himself upright and she was instantly thrown into weak confusion by the virile masculinity evident in every hard line of his big male body, his eyes dark and glittering as they stared down into hers.

'Like this, for a start.' She felt his hand at the nape of her neck, and when, in the next moment, the soft pale silk of her hair was released from its confining knot she gave a squawk of protest that made the cruel mouth twist in amusement. 'That's better.'

The satisfaction in his voice should have irritated her but didn't, and her annoyance was feigned as she said, 'What on earth do you think you're doing?'

'I wanted to do that this morning.' His eyes were holding hers with a searing intensity that made her breathless. 'Among other things,' he added softly.

'Colt—'

'But you were so very correct, so efficient.' His voice was like a warm caress moving all over her body, its touch electric. 'And so beautiful.'

'I really don't think this is helping either of us,' she said stiffly as she desperately tried to grab the last remaining shreds of sanity. 'You said you had a problem?'

'I'd promised myself I wouldn't approach you again until this damn job was completed,' he continued as if she hadn't spoken. 'I'd made up my mind not to give you any excuse for further accusations that I was trying to buy you by advancing your career. But...' He paused, his dark head tilted slightly to one side as his gaze wandered over her face, lingering on the softness of her mouth, before his lips claimed hers in a swift, possessive kiss that was all sensation. 'I can't,' he finished simply, raising his head from hers with obvious reluctance.

'Colt—'

'So the problem, my sweet little wench, is as much yours as mine. Somehow you've got in my blood.'

'You want me physically,' she stated baldly, using the crudity of the words as much against her own feelings as him. She knew what he wanted from his women, from her. He had been devastatingly honest right from the start—so how could she find herself on the verge of succumbing to what would be a brief affair for them both?

'Oh, I do, Jessica, I do.' There was a wicked amusement in his voice that did nothing to soothe her turmoil.

'And I've told you I'm not interested,' she said as firmly as the trembling deep inside her would allow.

'Then I'll just have to be satisfied with the pleasure of your company, won't I?' he drawled mockingly. 'Have dinner with me tonight?' The last few words were said in a different tone, something of a faint plea in the hard, husky voice which was incredibly sensual.

'I don't think there is any point,' she stated flatly.

'Well, I agree the sensible thing to do would be to go straight home to my big bed and put us both out of our misery, but failing that what's wrong with dinner?' he asked with a silky smoothness that didn't fool her for a minute.

'I don't want you to get the wrong idea.' She looked up at him as she spoke, just in time to see him close his eyes for an infinitesimal moment at her words.

'Jessica…' When he opened them again the grey eyes had taken on an almost silver hue that was mesmerising. 'How could I possibly get the wrong idea? You'd have crushed a lesser man to dust, and even my ego has its limits. Just get in the car, would you? There's a good girl. I promise dinner, that's all, and an evening spent in each other's company. Surely your soul is generous enough to spare a hungry man that brief indulgence?' The mockery was back, lazy and derisive, and as he glanced over her shoulder the wicked eyes sharpened. 'Here's a traffic warden—now you've got no choice.'

She found herself in the passenger seat of the Ferrari in the next second, Colt starting the engine just as the formidable little woman in black and yellow reached the car. 'Good evening.' Colt flashed his white teeth in something of a crocodile smile of satisfaction as the engine roared, and in the next moment the car had leapt into the evening traffic, taking its place with a regal indifference to the general herd that spoke of the personality of its driver.

'Where are we going?' Jessica asked when they had been travelling for some time through the late evening traffic, which was beginning to thin a little after the rush hour. The car windows were down and the air was warm and moist after the heat of the summer day. The soft suede interior of the car was combined with traditional leather, the seats both comfortable and luxurious, making the journey wonderfully relaxing compared to her normal fight home by tube.

'A little place I know.' He didn't glance at her as he spoke, his concentration fixed on the traffic, and she darted a brief look at his dark profile, her stomach turning over in spite of her effort to breathe deeply and remain composed. He was just so overwhelming, she thought weakly—but it was more than the striking good looks that turned her to jelly. It was the magnetic pull of that hard male personality, the sheer unadulterated power in the almost visible aura that surrounded him like a dark light. 'Put the TV on if you're bored.'

'What?' She jumped slightly as he spoke. Her musings had made her unaware that her eyes were still fixed on him, but now she saw he had been aware of her scrutiny as the slate-grey eyes flashed her way for a moment.

'The TV.' He indicated a small liquid-crystal screen in the dashboard where the radio would normally have been, that piece of equipment being mounted in the cabin roof. 'A high-tech toy to catch buyers, but it's been useful on occasions for my passengers when we've been in traffic—like now.'

He lived in a different world. She stared at the tiny TV, which suddenly seemed to epitomise the distance between her world and his. Not just in the way he thought and acted, but in the day-to-day things that could make all the difference between an easy ride and a blinding headache.

What did he know about fighting your way home on the tube after a lousy day at work, when everything had gone wrong, and your head was drumming with a tension migraine? Or queuing for hours in the supermarket and lugging heavy bags of shopping home which invariably broke at some crucial moment? Or eking out your salary at the end of a hard month and juggling the accounts in order to pay both Peter and Paul? Or—

'I've had many reactions to that little box, but never one of such ferocity.' The deep voice at her side brought her gaze swinging to his, the car having paused at traffic lights. 'What's the matter?' he asked quietly. 'What are you thinking?'

His words quickened the withdrawal that her thoughts had begun. She had vowed, when William had let her down so badly, that she would be her own person from that moment on. Her thoughts, her emotions, her heart would be her own until, if ever, she felt sufficiently secure in a relationship to be able to give them wholeheartedly without fear of rejection. Colt Irons was the last man on earth she would reveal her thoughts to—the very last.

'Nothing.' She smiled brightly and turned to look straight out of the windscreen.

'You can do better than that,' he said mockingly, his voice very dry. 'A simple lie would do.'

'You go in for lies, then?' she asked promptly, the car growling to be off as the lights changed to green.

'No, I don't go in for lies, Jessica.' His voice was quite expressionless but there was something, just something, that brought her head swinging round to his again. Some inflexion, the faintest indication she couldn't pin down, that made her think the words meant far more than their surface level suggested.

'Neither do I,' she said flatly, turning to face the front again.

'But you were thinking something,' he persisted smoothly, 'so "nothing" isn't exactly the truth, is it? Or don't half-truths count?'

He really was the most impossible man. She glared at him now, fairly simmering with outrage. How could he make her feel guilty about choosing to retain her privacy? But he had. 'I was just thinking how different we are,' she said tightly, before the incident got out of proportion. 'That's all.'

'Variety is the spice of life,' he drawled silkily.

'Oh, I'm sure you think so,' she agreed quickly, the note in her voice leaving him in no doubt as to what she was thinking.

'You disapprove of the TV?' he asked after a long, pregnant pause that told her her remark had been noted and filed.

'Of course not.' He wasn't going to leave it alone, was he?

'What, then?' he persisted quietly.

'I was just thinking…' Oh, there was no easy way to say it. 'It's just that you are in a different world from the average person, that's all. Privileged…'

'Rubbish.' The word was biting. 'If you are insinuating that I don't know what real life's about, forget it. I was brought up in a little fishing community in Rye and my father never had more than a few pounds to his name. My mother used to clean through the summer at some of the hotels in the area to provide my sister and me with the odd luxury, and she used every penny she earned to get us both through university.

'The sea took my father when he was fifty years old, in a ridiculous boating accident that wouldn't have happened if he'd had a better craft—which is one of the reasons why I make sure anything that has the Irons name on it is built to last—' He stopped abruptly, clearly regretting having revealed so much.

'And your mother?' she asked softly.

'She died later. Something happened... Something happened that broke her heart.' The tone was final, indicating that the conversation was closed. 'I use my wealth and my success, Jessica; I don't rely on it or allow it to isolate me from normal life. I have a couple of nice homes, cars, but if it all went tomorrow I'd cope just fine. That's the way it is.'

'I see.' She glanced at him again but he was looking straight ahead, his profile grim.

'No, you don't, but no matter. If it makes you feel good seeing me with horns and a forked tail, so be it,' he returned with cutting scorn.

'I didn't say that,' she protested indignantly.

'You didn't have to.' She saw him take a long, deep, hard breath and his voice was quieter when next he spoke. 'You really are the damnedest woman.'

'Others have said the same.' As she repeated the words he had used that night in the restaurant he glanced at her once, sharply, and then laughed softly, the sound appreciative.

'Now, I suspect that, unlike when I said it, that's not quite true,' he said dryly, in the deep, husky voice that turned her toes into curling pads.

'Careful, you're verging on being gracious again,' she warned softly, and then her heart turned over, thudding against her chest, as he really laughed out loud for the first time in their acquaintance. The sound was rich and deep and carefree, and she suspected he didn't make it too often, but it was the fierce pleasure it gave her that caused her blood to freeze.

She was getting in too deep. The warning was there, stark and clear. It didn't matter that she had only known him a matter of weeks—where this man was concerned one meeting would be enough to get hooked. But she wasn't, she told herself firmly. Of course she wasn't hooked. Once bitten, twice shy—and she'd been nearly savaged to death six months ago.

They ate at a beautiful little restaurant tucked away in its own grounds on the outskirts of London, horseshoe-shaped stone steps leading to a secluded little patio away from the main dining room. The tiled floor was spangled in the evening sun and the air was fragrant with sweet-smelling shrubs and flowers in huge terracotta pots, the large lawn beyond dominated by a crystal-clear pool complete with dancing fountain and a chubby little cherub.

'What a gorgeous place.' Jessica felt she had been transported to paradise. 'It's enchanting. It was fortunate this part outside wasn't taken—it's such a warm night.'

'This is not normally used.' Colt's eyes were narrowed on her face. 'But I'm on good terms with the owner.'

'Oh, I see. He's a friend of yours?' she asked politely, taking a sip of the ice-cold sparkling white wine the waiter had served a few moments before when he had collected their order. It tasted wonderful.

'In a manner of speaking.' At her raised eyebrows he smiled easily. 'I bought the place about five years ago. The then owner had got into financial difficulties and the place was very run-down and losing money hand over fist. I gutted the place, had the grounds landscaped and so on, and added this particular arbour for my private use.

'The chef is a French guy I went through university with who is second to none. I poached him from his then employment—' it was said without the faintest shred of contrition '—and gave him a free hand with staff, kitchen equipment and so on. The result has been very good,' he added. 'I've doubled the staff since then, but we still can only just keep up with demand, and now the reservations are creeping into weeks ahead, I understand.'

'You have the Midas touch.' She smiled at him but he didn't smile back.

'With business, it would seem.' Evening had brought

a mellowed softness to the light and there was a sense
of whispering stillness as he moved across, bringing his
dark head down to her pale blonde one. The kiss was
warm and sweet—too warm and too sweet in view of
the immediate physical rapport that sprang into life. And
although it only lasted a minute or two her whole body
was aching with slumberous sensation when he slid back
into his own seat, taking a long, hard pull at his drink
as though nothing had happened between them. 'Sorry,
a slight lapse,' he said with lazy mockery, but she was
saved from having to formulate some sort of reply that
wouldn't reveal her shattered emotions by the arrival of
the waiter with their first course.

The food was wonderful, she was conscious of that
much, but it could have been coated in sawdust for all
the impression it made on her. She wasn't going to be
able to do this again. As the courses came and went,
each one a work of art in itself, the conviction grew.
Like before, Colt had set himself out to be charming and
amusing and the spell he wove was powerful, entering
into the very quintessence of her mind.

Every moment spent in his company was a moment
of flirting with danger; she *knew* that. So why had she
come? she asked herself faintly. What was she doing,
testing herself? Playing some weird game to see how
strong she had become? Well, not strong enough; that
last kiss had told her that. The temptation to take what
he was offering—to allow herself the luxury of running
her hands over his hard body, across the range of muscle
and sinew clothed in firm, tanned flesh, to allow the need
that became more sweet, more potent every minute she
spent with him to take control of her thoughts and actions—was growing stronger and stronger.

But theirs wouldn't be a normal relationship; he had
told her that. There would be no chance of shared intimacy and tenderness developing into anything more; the
tight buds of physical pleasure wouldn't open and
bloom—not on his side anyway. And on hers? She

would be consumed, utterly consumed. The knowledge ruined the last of her appetite.

By the time they left the restaurant the moon was shedding a thin, hollow light over the pool, causing the dancing water to shimmer and shatter in tiny diamond droplets, and she knew she would remember this bitter-sweet evening for the rest of her life.

'Straight home? Or would you prefer a coffee at my place?' It wouldn't be just a coffee—the dark, hungry gleam in his eyes told her that—and she answered quickly, her voice a little too high.

'Home, please.'

He had parked the Ferrari in a large alcove off the main car park, which she realised now was his own private parking space, and at her tone he leant back in his seat, stretching his legs lazily before putting one arm along the back of her seat as he half turned to her. 'Face the truth, Jessica. You want me just as much as I want you. This...fire between us, this attraction, it doesn't happen often—take it from one who knows.' The last words had an edge of cynical mockery that hurt her. 'Why prolong the agony when our relationship can only have one conclusion?'

'We don't have a relationship,' she bit back tightly.

'You're telling those half-truths again.' His voice was a slow drawl and suddenly the confidence he was displaying, the assumption that she was going to fall in his arms like all those other women, hit her on the raw, causing her mouth to tighten and her eyes to shoot black sparks.

'Our relationship is no different from the one you have with any of your other employees,' she stated flatly. 'Like Danielle...or Jack.' Quite what made her bring the name of his personal assistant into the conversation at that point she didn't know, but she used it almost as a talisman, a defence against the desire in those lethal grey eyes.

She felt him stiffen, the arm at the back of her shoulders tensing as hard muscles contracted, but his face was perfectly expressionless as he said, 'I've never wined and dined Jack Goode, Jessica.'

'You know what I mean,' she snapped angrily.

'He likes you, you know that, don't you?' The lazy assurance was all gone, his eyes dark and glittering. 'Are you attracted to him?'

'He…he's been very helpful.'

'Oh, I just bet he has.' His voice was pure ice, freezing her thought process. 'Well, you can forget about Jack Goode, Jessica. He isn't your type.'

The utter arrogance took her breath away and she actually gasped before rallying sufficiently to glare back at him, her mouth thinning with rage. 'How dare you? You've no idea what my type is—'

'I'm your type.' His arms were bands of steel tightening round her body and this time the brake that had been applied before was gone. He pulled her into the hard planes of him, crushing her body to his, his mouth burningly possessive. 'I'll prove it.' And then his mouth took hers again, his tongue thrustingly erotic.

She struggled, but the twists and turns of her body merely inflamed them both, his hands shaping the small of her back as he moved her sensually against him before they rose up to her waist, and then the soft, warm swell of her breasts, where they burnt through the material of her dress like fire. She was melting, hardly aware of what was happening to her as reason and sanity were caught up in a torrent of sexual excitement that was overpoweringly fierce.

She could have fought harder if he had been violent, if he had used brute force, but he applied just enough strength to subdue her struggles at the same time as maintaining a sensual assault that was unrelentingly pleasurable. She wasn't aware that the buttons to her dress had been undone until she felt his fingers cupping her aching breasts, and his ministrations to their swollen fullness were so exquisite that they drove lucid thought

still further into the recesses of her mind. But then, as
his dark head bent to take possession of what his fingers
had held, and she felt a piercing thrill of tormenting pleasure spear her through, she realised just what she was
allowing.

'No! No, please—please don't.' She spoke the words
on a thick sob, barely coherent. 'I don't want this.'

'Jessica?' Her name was a question and now her voice
was stronger as she twisted away from him, pressing her
back against the passenger door as she fumbled desperately with the tiny gold buttons on the bodice of her
dress.

'I won't be just another of your women, Colt. I
can't...I'm not made like that. I shouldn't have let you
think—'

He swore softly, the sound ugly in the soft night air,
but as she flinched he ran a shaking hand through his
hair, his face torn with so many emotions she couldn't
have named just one. 'The fault is mine; we both know
that. You made it perfectly plain how you feel, and for
the first time in my life I allowed my feelings to govern
my actions. Jessica—'

'Just take me home.' She cut into his words with a
sharpness that bordered on hysteria as a mixture of
shame, embarrassment and deep, deep hurt made her
want to curl into a tiny little ball somewhere and die.

'We need to talk, damn it—'

'I'll walk if I have to.' Her eyes were wild and his
narrowed gaze searched her strained features as he nodded slowly.

'All right, Jessica.' His voice was cool and detached,
the sort of soothing, remote tone one would apply to a
distressed, lost child, and the sound cut her to ribbons.
If he had needed further proof that she just wasn't in his
realm, that his world was an alien place she could never
fit into, she had just supplied it most effectively. He was
the remote, cold tycoon of daylight hours again, a law

unto himself, and she doubted if he would ever bother with her again.

So why wasn't she feeling relief, a thankfulness that it was finally over? Any one of a number of emotions should be present with the knowledge that this dangerous episode of her life was finished, but all she felt was pain and bitter confusion.

He didn't say a word on the drive home through the dark, shadowed streets, but the silence was thick and black and heavy. She had the feeling he couldn't wait to be rid of her. She had never felt so small or lost in her life, and she couldn't understand the gnawing misery inside her.

They exchanged a stilted goodbye before she sprang out of the car, in a repeat of the time before, as it drew to a smooth halt outside the house. But this time the Ferrari had leapt away before she had time to turn her key in the lock, the powerful machine echoing his disgust with her.

She stood for some minutes on the doorstep, long after the sound of the car had disappeared, the night air soft and balmy with the unmistakable tang peculiar to all big cities. It was only the sound of the telephone in the hall that drove her indoors.

She picked the receiver up tentatively—she had never felt less like talking to anyone in her life but the other residents of the house were either asleep or pretending to be. 'Hello?'

'I'm very sorry to bother you at this late hour but it is important. Could I speak to Jessica Taylor, please?' Her mother's voice was as determined as always.

'It's me speaking, Mother.' What now? Now of all nights?

'Jessica, darling.' The tones were honeyed. 'Have I disturbed you?'

'I've just got in.' She knew her attitude wasn't conducive to a harmonious exchange, but right now the very last thing in all the world she wanted was to talk to her mother. 'What is it?'

'I didn't want you to hear it through anyone else.' And then she knew, even before the soft voice continued, 'It's Jo and William, darling. They had a little girl at six o'clock this evening.'

CHAPTER SIX

THE following few weeks until Colt's project was completed were painful and tense, but at last it was done, and done well. There had been various meetings over that time, some involving the great man himself and others with Jack and the various contacts Jessica had organised, and when Colt had been present he had been icily polite and studiously correct.

Jack had asked her for a date, as she had suspected he would, and she'd refused him—which had surprised her, as she had told herself she would say yes. She liked him—in fact she thought he was lovely—but whatever spark needed to be there just wasn't, and she had learnt enough from the William episode to realise it couldn't be manufactured.

When her mother had told her about Jo's baby she hadn't felt anything beyond a faint sadness that she had a niece whom she would rarely, if ever, see. And it was in that moment, and only then, that she had realised her love for William had been of the lukewarm variety that easily cooled. The knowledge had horrified and unnerved her more than she could explain to herself. If Jo hadn't stepped in, if William hadn't betrayed her, she would be married to him now and her life would be inexorably linked with his. And it would have been a mistake.

Oh, they might have had some kind of domesticated happiness, drifting on into family life with the traditional 2.4 children and all the trappings, but she would have been living a second-best existence without knowing it.

Her mother had said much the same thing the night that she had told her of the birth.

'How do you feel about it?' she'd asked, after a long pause when Jessica hadn't said a word. 'You were obviously expecting the news some time soon?'

'I hadn't really thought about it,' Jessica had said honestly, a note of surprise in her voice that the older woman had recognised with a little dart of thankfulness. 'I've been so busy lately, what with work and so on. But I'm pleased for Jo, if that's what she wants.'

'I don't think Jo knows what she wants,' her mother said with a touch of tartness. 'She's not happy—but there it is; it's done now. You can really say that and mean it, Jessica?' she asked softly. 'About being pleased for her, I mean?'

'Yes, in a way.' Jessica thought for a moment and her voice was stronger as she affirmed, 'Yes, I'm pleased for her. William too. He wasn't right for me but I didn't realise it at the time.'

'I did,' her mother said promptly. 'He's a wind and water man, Jessica. This whole miserable affair confirmed every doubt I'd always had about him.'

'You never said.' Jessica's voice was high with surprise at the damning verdict.

'I did, darling, but you'd never listen,' her mother said softly. 'You've always had the idea I don't care for you, haven't you? But you're wrong; I care for you very much. The problem is, you are very much like me and that's why we tend to clash more than a little. But I love you, Jessica; I always have. I know you blame me partly for Jo and William, but I had no idea what was going on.'

'I don't blame you, not now,' Jessica said quietly.

'But you did.' Her mother sighed deeply. 'We seem to have got our wires crossed so often over the years, don't we? And I know the fault is mine. When I left your father…' There was a long pause and her mother's voice was thick when she continued, 'I was in a mess emotionally, Jessica.'

'Mother, this is old history—'

'No, I want you to understand,' Mrs Taylor said urgently. 'I never stopped loving him, Jessica, he knew that, but I just couldn't live with him any more. His work was his mistress, always, and in the end she won. I was tired of competing, tired of trying to bring up two children alone, tired of having no permanent home, of losing friends, of always being on my own. The affair with John…it was just a means of actually forcing myself to leave; that's why it didn't last two minutes. I shall never love anyone but your father but I'm too jealous to share him, especially because I know I can never win. His work is his first love.'

Jessica stared at the phone, stunned, unable to take in what her mother was revealing. It was too much, after the evening she'd had, and then the news about Jo and William. This further bombshell was just too much.

'But don't think I don't love you, darling. You've always been very special to me, something Jo has always sensed and deeply resented. I think it was probably that which first prompted this graceful affair with William.'

'Oh, Mum…' Jessica was crying now, and for a few moments there was loud sniffing at both ends of the phone.

'I've telephoned your father with the news,' Mrs Taylor said after a minute or so, her voice thick but controlled. 'He's still very angry on your behalf, of course. He does love you so, as do I. But you do understand Jo needs someone? I'm disgusted and horrified at the pair of them, but I can't abandon Jo.'

'I don't expect you to.' They spoke for several more minutes and when at last Jessica had put down the phone she stood leaning against the wall for long moments, her head whirling. How could one phone call erase the hurt and pain of years? But it had. If only they had talked like this before. If only she had been more discerning, had sensed her mother's pain.

But her mother was right, she mused now: they were too much alike, too good at hiding their feelings and coping, at getting on with things—although she had blessed that strength several times in the last few weeks, during the meetings with Colt.

Still, it was over now. Jessica flexed her toes in the warm, silky water of the bath she had run for herself on getting home from work, allowing her thoughts to concentrate fully on Colt and the finished job. There would be no more sensing his deadly gaze from across the room, no more curt, terse conversations, no more checking and re-checking to make sure every little fact was spot-on, no more working into the early hours. So why did she feel so downright miserable? She wriggled irritably, feeling thoroughly out of sorts with herself. She was stupid, pathetic, and it had to stop. She'd made her decision for better or worse that night in his car and that was that. No post mortems, not another one.

Tomorrow she would go out in her lunch hour and buy something new, something ridiculously expensive, and perhaps even get her hair shaped into a different style at the weekend. She was young and healthy and she had everything in life to look forward to. *She had.* She emerged from the bath in a determined mood that carried her through the evening with friends at a nightclub, and into a deep, dreamless sleep in the early hours from which she awoke refreshed and ready for another hectic working day.

She was just gobbling down a slice of toast before racing out of the house when one of the other occupants banged on her door. 'Phone, Jessica!'

'Who is it?' She opened the door as quickly as she could but Janie had already disappeared in a flurry of red hair and black tights, behind schedule as always.

Whoever it was they were going to have to be quick, she thought militantly as she took the stairs two at a time. She couldn't be late for work again. 'Yes?' She tried to be polite but the impatience showed.

'Jessica?' The deep, husky voice that was indelibly printed in the core of her being set her heart thudding frantically. 'I won't keep you a moment. Are you free on Saturday evening?'

'I...' She was dumbstruck, numb with shock.

'I want to take you and Russell out, as a thank-you for a job well done,' he continued smoothly. 'And Russell and Monica are free Saturday, so he suggested I check with you.'

Did he? Well, thanks, Russell; thanks a bunch, she thought desperately as her heart continued to pound. What should she do? How could she say no if the other two had accepted? 'A thank-you?' she repeated tentatively, her mind racing with a hundred replies. 'But that's not necessary.'

'Nevertheless, I'd like to do it,' Colt said pleasantly. 'And Russell seemed delighted.'

Well, he would, wouldn't he? she thought faintly. To be seen wining and dining with Colt Irons couldn't do Russell's little business any harm at all.

'If you can't make it Saturday we'll arrange a night in the week,' Colt went on, the thread of steel she recognised from conversations in the past making itself known. So that was how it was; he wasn't going to allow her to duck out of this. It was her and Russell together or nothing, and, knowing Russell as he now did, Colt must be fully aware she would have to say yes to keep her boss happy.

But she didn't have anything to lose, she thought suddenly. Colt had made it abundantly clear over the last few weeks that any attraction he might have had for her was well and truly dead, so this was probably just a polite gesture to end their acquaintance on a conciliatory note. It was horribly presumptuous on her part to think anything else, she thought with a dart of embarrassment.

'Saturday is fine,' she said quickly. 'If you're sure you want to do this.'

'I'm quite sure, Jessica.' The dark voice was faintly wicked, with a mockery that caused the pink in her cheeks to deepen, and she was unutterably thankful that those piercing grey eyes weren't around to see her confusion. 'I'll arrange a taxi for seven—'

'Oh, there's no need—'

'Which will already have picked up Russell and Monica.' The mockery was open now, and her cheeks were scarlet as she muttered a hasty goodbye before putting down the phone. She hated him, she really hated him, she thought savagely, racing frantically about the bedsit before catapulting out into the street ten minutes late for her usual tube. She refused to recognise the trembling excitement that had speared through her the moment she had heard his voice. He was arrogant, high-handed, overbearing...

Russell was like a dog with two tails when she reached the office, his small, portly frame fairly bristling with delight at the invitation, which she heard him mention to anyone and everyone at regular intervals throughout the day until it made her want to scream.

Thank goodness it was Friday tomorrow, she thought wryly as she left the office that night. If Colt had proffered his invitation on a Monday she wouldn't have been surprised if Russell had arranged a suitable announcement in the papers as to their dining venue!

Saturday morning she called in at the hairdresser's, deciding at the last moment not to have her hair cut short but to compromise with a soft, feathery layered look that fell about her face and shoulders in shining silky wisps of silver. She spent the rest of the day shopping, searching for something special for the night ahead. She couldn't rationalise how she felt, but the memory of Colt's uncompromising coolness and terse politeness over the last few weeks rankled in spite of all her efforts to master her feelings, and she was determined that for this last time they would meet she would at least look as good as she could.

He had been able to dismiss his attraction for her without a shred of regret, and that was fine—of course it was, she told herself tightly as she marched from shop to shop. But she was blowed if she was going to sneak away from this last encounter like a small whipped dog. No, she'd go out with a bang, show him she could handle herself just as well as any of the beauties he frequently escorted. And with Russell and Monica present there would be no danger of Colt getting the wrong idea. Perfect.

She found a dress in the very last shop she entered, which was also the most expensive. But as soon as she laid eyes on the short silk cocktail dress in pale coffee, with a matching thigh-length jacket, she knew it was the one. The minky tone of the material emphasised the darkness of her eyes, whilst throwing her pale ash-blonde hair into shimmering relief, complementing her creamy skin and fine, even features. She gulped a little at the price, but only a little. She would have paid twice as much to look good that evening.

And so it was that when she heard the taxi driver ring the bell at precisely seven o'clock she was able to walk down the stairs feeling at least partially in control, despite the racing butterflies that seemed as though they were competing for the Olympics in her stomach.

Only it wasn't the taxi driver who was standing on the steps. 'Jessica…' He seemed to be able to put an inflexion on her name that no one else did, giving it a dark sensuality that turned her bones to liquid. 'I'm speechless.'

Colt Irons lost for words? Never. 'I doubt that.' She managed a cool smile she was proud of. 'Where's…?' As her gaze swept up and down the street she felt the smile falter. There was no taxi. No Russell and Monica. Just that devastatingly wicked car parked a few yards away, the passenger door swung open with an impudence that made her see red.

'You said there'd be a taxi, that you were picking up Russell and Monica first.' Her eyes shot back to his, her face flushing with outrage at the knowledge that he had fooled her, lied to her. Was Russell in on the conspiracy? Was that it? Or perhaps Colt was driving her to the restaurant to meet them? Well, she could cope with that—just. 'Are we meeting them at the restaurant?' she asked tightly, her eyes swinging back to the Ferrari.

'Not exactly.' And he actually had the gall to smile. 'There's been a change of plan. You see—'

'Are we meeting them at all?' Her voice was stony now, her body stiffening as she took a step backwards into the house. He wouldn't…would he? He wouldn't have planned some sort of last fling seduction scene?

'No, you see—'

As she went to slam the door in his face he moved quickly, his foot shooting over the threshold at the same time as his shoulder took the force of the wood, making him wince, but she was so angry she was barely aware of it. 'How dare you? How *dare* you pretend it was an evening for Russell and Monica too, when all the time you were planning this?' she snapped furiously. 'That's disgusting, absolutely disgusting. Well, you can take a running jump, Colt Irons; there is no way I'm going anywhere with you. If you want to plan a sad, tawdry little seduction scene call on one of your all too willing admirers to oblige, but count me out! I wouldn't go out with you if you were the last man on earth—'

'Have you quite finished?' he said in a voice that was deceptively soft.

'I haven't even started—'

'Wrong, dead wrong.' And to her horror she found herself lifted up into the air, slung over his shoulder and carried down the steps towards the Ferrari as though she were a sack of potatoes. She began to twist and struggle, and then felt a resounding smack on her behind just as they reached the car, with a muttered, 'Be still, woman.'

She was so stunned with shock that he had dumped her into the luxurious interior and slid into the driving seat beside her before she could find either her voice or her legs. But when she reached for the handle his growl stopped the movement mid-flow. 'Don't push me one iota further, Jessica, or I swear I won't be responsible for my actions.'

'You... I won't... You can't force me to go with you.' He ignored her splutterings with icy disdain, starting the engine and pulling away from the kerb even as she spoke. 'I mean it, Colt; I'll jump out if you don't stop,' she warned, panic gripping her throat.

'No, you won't.' He didn't glance at her but she could tell he was angry, furiously angry, his face dark with the force of his emotion. 'If you make one movement, just one, I'll stop this car and put you over my knee.'

'Don't be so ridiculous.' But he meant it, she knew he meant it, and humiliating though it was she was forced to bite her tongue and keep still as the car leapt through the summer evening.

'What have you come here for?' As they screeched to a stop in the emergency car park of one of London's hospitals she stared at him in amazement. But he still didn't speak, pulling her from the car after he had walked round and opened her door with an energy that told her his control was paper-thin.

'I'm not moving until you tell me—' Her words were cut short as he took her arm, thrusting her slightly in front of him as he practically frog-marched her into the building.

'Can I help you?'

The pretty receptionist in the maternity wing was all smiles as her big blue eyes fastened on Colt's dark face, and he was all charm in return as he said, 'A Mrs Monica Roberts? Could you tell me if she's here?'

'Certainly.' The receptionist looked faintly puzzled but consulted a large book. 'Yes, Mrs Roberts is on Muskett Ward at the moment, but—'

'And could you tell us what time she was admitted?'

'Earlier this morning.' The receptionist was clearly smitten, her eyes hungry as she looked into Colt's grey gaze. 'But I understand the birth is imminent.'

'Thank you.' Colt smiled and the blue eyes all but glazed over as that lethal magnetism made the air crackle.

'Is there a message?' she asked quickly. 'Your name…?'

'Just tell Mrs Roberts and her husband that the dinner will have to be a post-birth celebration,' Colt said smoothly. 'If you could? They'll understand.'

'Oh, certainly, certainly,' the receptionist gushed dreamily.

Once outside in the warmth of the summer evening, the faint odour of antiseptic wafting through the open glass doors, Jessica turned to Colt, nerving herself for what was possibly the worst moment of her life. 'I'm sorry.' It was totally inadequate in view of all she had said, she thought helplessly. 'I jumped to conclusions I had no right to assume.'

'That you did.' His voice was quite expressionless now, his eyes hooded as he looked down at her for a long moment before taking her hand in his and urging her forward. 'Come on; we're blocking the doorway and I'd hate for some unfortunate woman not to make it because we're in the way.'

She had never felt so small or so utterly, completely mortified as she walked by his side to the car. 'They phoned me at just after four,' he said quietly as they reached the Ferrari. 'Apparently Russell had been trying to get you for most of the day, but you were out.'

'I was shopping.' She didn't know how to face him, keeping her eyes downwards as he opened the door for her to slide into the car. The beautiful silk of the dress mocked her now as she kept her eyes on her hands, which were clasped tightly in her lap. All that planning, all that effort to convince him she was an elegant, sophisticated woman, in her own right, and what had she done? Blown it. Oh… She shut her eyes tightly for a moment as he joined her in the car. How she'd blown it.

'And I tried to phone you at half past four, then five, then half past…'

'I didn't get in till after six.' This was awful, terrible. What was he going to do now? Drop her home? Humiliating as that would be, it was preferable to trying to salvage some normality out of the excruciatingly painful mess.

'What is it about me you can't stand, Jessica?' The words brought her head jerking upright to stare into the dark grey eyes. 'I know you are physically attracted to me, but me as a person, a human being? What is it you find so damn hard to take?'

'It's not like that,' she whispered painfully, and then jumped as his voice barked into the space between them.

'The hell it isn't! I know this fiancé of yours gave you a rough deal—' He stopped abruptly and took a long, hard breath before continuing, 'But you are intelligent enough to know that all men don't play that sort of two-timing game. I can understand you don't want any romantic attachments at the moment; it's too soon. But the animosity, the sheer hostility you've shown since we first met… You want me, and you're fighting it every inch of the way; that's the truth, isn't it?'

His eyes were blazing as they held hers but for the life of her she couldn't speak. 'Do you think I'm totally to blame for this attraction between us; is that it? Because believe me, girl, I could do without it.'

'I…I couldn't just sleep with anyone—'

'And you think I could? You think one-night stands are my scene; is that it? *Damn it, Jessica!*' As he started the engine she sat huddled in her seat, feeling that if the sky dropped in and the world ended at that moment she couldn't feel worse than how she was feeling now. She'd made a mistake, a colossal, gargantuan giant of a mistake, but how could she explain it was her own feelings of vulnerability where he was concerned that had made her so suspicious and distrustful?

She couldn't. The very telling would reveal exactly

what she had to keep from him at all costs: *that she loved him*. No... As it dawned on her in all its blazing horror she knew she had been fighting it from the moment she had first laid eyes on him. Madness, emotional suicide—oh, yes, all that and much, much more, she told herself desperately. But this was no rebound attraction after William's betrayal, no mere titillation of the physical senses. She loved him.

She had never believed in love at first sight; such a concept was unacceptable, she had thought in all her pre-Colt arrogance. But oh... she gazed blindly out of the window as the car sped on...she was paying for that innocently held belief now.

If he hadn't exploded into her world with all the force of a bright black meteor, she might have gone on thinking she had loved William, that his betrayal had been a disaster, that she had had the best snatched from her. But nothing had hurt her like this; nothing ever would. She loved a man who was incapable of returning that commitment—who couldn't, wouldn't, ever want more than a brief, physical affair for as long as it took for the novelty to wear off, for someone else to come onto his horizon, someone younger—or older—someone different, to spark the interest of a jaded palate.

She was so sunk in misery that it was some time before she realised they weren't on the route back to her bedsit. 'Where are we going?' Her voice was small and flat and he glanced at her once before answering.

'Do you feel up to sitting in a restaurant, eating in front of a crowd of other people?' His voice was grim.

'No, but—'

'Neither do I. I'll phone the restaurant once we reach my apartment.' She didn't dare question his choice of destination in view of what had gone before, but he continued as though she had done so. 'And I am quite capable of entertaining a woman in my home without leaping on her—' his voice was a study in blankness '—so rest assured you will emerge from the wolf's den un-scathed.'

She didn't answer. There was absolutely nothing she could say, and they both knew it.

CHAPTER SEVEN

COLT'S apartment was exactly what would be expected of an astute millionaire playboy with the world at his feet, and that in itself hurt her.

She had learnt enough about this cool, complex man over the last few weeks to know that the real Colt Irons was locked away deep inside the cynical outer shell— but the layers were inches thick. This severely luxurious, very male apartment, with its black leather furniture and thick dove-grey carpets, was the ultimate in bachelor pads, with a range of buttons on the hand-held control to work absolutely everything from the full-length drapes at the windows to the massive TV... Nothing of the personality of the man who owned it was on view— not one photograph was on display, and there were no ornaments, no plants, no softness.

'Well?' He glanced at her now as he fixed their drinks, the grey eyes narrowed and dark. 'What do you think of my home from home?'

'Home from home?' She eagerly picked up on the words, hoping he wouldn't press her to give an opinion of the apartment. It was magnificent and impressive...and she hated it.

'My real home is down in Hastings,' he said quietly as he walked across to her with lazy grace, handing her a glass of white wine before sitting on the large, bulky settee opposite her chair, one leg crossed over the other as he settled back against the leather. 'But I'm rarely there. Work commitments keep me tied to the city pretty much all the time these days.'

'Oh, I see. And it was sensible to buy an apartment rather than stay in hotels all the time?' she said carefully.

His easy pose of calm relaxation was not having that effect on her at all—in fact, she had never felt so tense in her life. He looked big and dark and dangerous as he sat there watching her. And impossibly attractive.

'Just so.' He smiled, but it didn't reach the glittering eyes. 'Living out of a suitcase became tiresome and this place was adequate for my purposes. The security is excellent, and as most of the tenants are in the same position as myself privacy is guaranteed.'

A nice, discreet residence where no questions were asked, but without the cosiness of fireside and slippers to give a girl the wrong idea, Jessica thought perceptively. Yes, she could see why this beautiful, aloof shell of a place would suit a man like Colt. When they had first entered the gracious wood-panelled hall he had waved her through to the massive sitting room before phoning the restaurant, cancelling their table and requesting the meal be brought round to his apartment—causing her to reflect on the power of influence and wealth.

She had also wondered, with a sick twist to her heart, how many other times the apartment had seen the same scenario played out, and that thought was at the forefront of her mind now as he gestured towards the stereo, which was playing a lazy, soft ballad. 'Would you prefer a different type of music?' he asked quietly. 'Jazz perhaps, or classical?'

'No, this is fine.' She had answered too quickly and too sharply, and she tried to moderate her voice as she continued, 'I wonder how Monica's doing?'

'Monica?' The grey eyes had darkened to onyx, the artificial light overhead throwing no colour into his jet-black hair. And then the thick, curling lashes hid his eyes for a moment as he inclined his head downwards before repeating Russell's wife's name. 'Monica—yes, of course. I'm sure she's doing okay. Would you like me to phone the hospital and see if there's any news?'

'No, it's all right.' Her gaze flickered as his fastened

on her again, and she hoped it wasn't too obvious that her use of Monica's name had been more to defuse an atmosphere that was suddenly too intimate than anything else.

She had felt vulnerable before admitting the truth to herself—but now the knowledge that she loved him, that the sweet, overpowering need he induced so easily had more than lustful attraction at its root, was terrifying. What was she going to do? she thought painfully, vitally aware that one slip, one revealing gesture or word, and he would know he had her exactly where he wanted her. How was she going to cope with an evening that had been turned on its heels, the very proper social occasion she had envisaged lost somewhere in the space between his body and hers?

'Relax, Jessica.' The dark voice was very dry. 'Don't you know it's the height of crassness to make a move before you've wined and dined the lady?'

'This isn't funny—'

'You're telling me.' The ruthlessly handsome features could have been set in granite as his eyes held hers, their greyness as sharp as polished stone. And then his face changed, softened, as he said, 'For the first time in my life I don't know what to say, and I agree—it isn't funny.'

No, don't you dare do this, she thought weakly, the shock of his words bringing her head bolt upright and making her back stiffen. A sensual assault on her body, a determination to subdue and subjugate her to his will—those things she could understand and fight. But the insidious weakness that had pulsed through her body as he had admitted his uncertainty had her wanting to move across and smooth all the cynicism from his handsome face.

Did he know how incredibly sensual that mix of 'hard man of the world' and 'little boy lost' was? Oh, yes, he knew. The answer was there but it hurt her to acknowledge it. He had been quite honest about what he wanted in the rules of play, and it wasn't Colt who had changed—she had.

'Colt, I've told you how it is.' She tried to be matter-of-fact and cool, but she was aware of the hectic flush in her cheeks and the rapid beating of her heart and that didn't help her confidence an iota. 'I don't want a quick affair—'

'Neither do I.' He grinned at her and it was all she could do not to leap into his arms as the hard male face softened into that younger one again. 'It definitely wouldn't be quick, Jessica, I promise you.'

'You know what I mean.' She glared at him but with that new knowledge at the forefront of her mind her heart wasn't in it. And, like a wolf sensing a ripe little lamb ready for the taking, he sensed it.

'Come here...' He stood up in one lithe movement, his face suddenly tense but wonderfully tender, and she found herself rising too, even as she knew it would only take one kiss for things to get out of hand.

Stop this, *stop it*, she told herself, but the warning was empty as he moved across the space between them. 'Poor little Jessica...' His voice was sexy and warm and soft as he took her in his arms. 'All alone in the big bad wolf's lair.'

'Colt—'

'Shh.' He moved her slightly from him, raising her chin with one finger as he stared down into the velvet darkness of her eyes. 'You're beautiful, Jessica, so beautiful. Beautiful and brave and everything a man could want.' The kisses were tiny and feather-light as they moved over her forehead and nose, her eyes closing as his warm lips brushed over her eyelids, their touch erotic. When he turned his attention to her throat and ears she moaned, hearing the sound with a little throb of dismay, but utterly unable to do anything about it.

'This isn't so very terrible, is it...?' There was a sus-picion of amusement in the husky voice but she didn't care. She didn't care about anything but the whirlpool of pleasure he was creating so easily. 'We can take it nice and slow, as slow as you want, I promise you.'

As his tongue parted her lips and the kiss changed tempo into one of sensual possessiveness she knew what was going to happen. She couldn't fight him, she didn't want to fight him—tomorrow would have to take care of itself. Was it so wrong to want some time with him—be it weeks, months—before it ended, as it inevitably would? Surely she had the right to some memories to warm her through the years when he was out of her orbit for good, when her career would have to be husband and lover and friend?

As he eased her closer into the hard male frame of him she could feel his arousal, hot and strong, against her softness. If she didn't sleep with him she wouldn't sleep with anyone; she knew that now. And she wanted him, wanted to know what it was like to be joined to the pulsating force of his manhood, wanted to share the intimacy of waking to his shape beside hers in the morning. It might be for a short time but that was better than nothing...wasn't it?

'You've no idea how you make me feel. I've been eating you, sleeping you, breathing you for weeks.' His mouth was against hers as he spoke, his voice ragged with desire, and she shuddered at what it did to the pure heat rising in the core of her. She was melting, locked against him in an embrace that was all-consuming, his hands roaming over her body and creating little rivulets of fire wherever they touched.

'Do you want me, Jessica? Do you?' His voice was urgent, his hands hungry. 'Tell me...'

And she was just about to comply, to admit that the need of him was overpowering, torrential, when the little buzz from the machine by the door piped up with intrusive determination. She felt Colt stiffen and then he swore softly, with deadly intent, before raising his head from hers with a rueful smile. 'The damn food.' He shook his head, raking back his hair and taking a deep, hard pull of air. 'What timing.'

She managed a shaky smile in reply, adjusting her clothing with trembling fingers as he walked swiftly out of the room. She heard him speak to the commissionaire, confirming he had ordered the food and asking him to send the delivery boy straight up, and she quickly took her seat again, taking several sips of wine in an effort to control her quivering limbs.

Within minutes the elegant dining table was full of dishes, steaming hot and wonderfully aromatic. And as Colt poured her another glass of wine, his eyes lazy as they stroked over her flushed face, the full enormity of what she had been about to do washed over her.

Was she mad? she asked herself helplessly. Stark, staring mad? How could she abandon the morals and values she had lived by for twenty-four years in the space of moments? Once he tired of her, as he had as good as told her he would, he would ask her to leave his life and she would be dispatched in the same way as the women before her. They might have been able to cope with that arrangement, but she couldn't—she just wasn't built that way.

She had to make him see, to stop what was to him merely a game to get her into his bed. The job was finished now, the pursuit was over; he *had* to understand. And how was she going to convince him? she asked herself, even as the answer that had been staring her in the face for weeks made itself known.

She would have to tell him, quite baldly and without any fancy words, that she wasn't the independent, career-minded woman of the world he wanted to see when he looked at her. That she hadn't slept with William, as she knew he assumed, that she hadn't slept with anyone. He was used to fast, racy women well versed in the arts of love who could hold down high-powered jobs, lovers, perhaps even husbands too. Who could juggle all the diverse facets of their lives with enormous success and emerge unscathed from the sort of liaison he was suggesting.

And she...she just wasn't in their league. She was going to make herself look naïve and foolish at best, hopelessly old-fashioned and more than a little pathetic at worst, and provide him with the best laugh he'd had in years. The last thought brought a shaft of pain that was unbearable. She didn't want him to remember her like that, she admitted to herself, which was why she had hesitated to spell it out. She had wanted to remain in his memory as the one that got away, a little different from the rest. Well, they said pride went before a fall...

'Colt?' She raised her head as she spoke, her plate of food untouched, to find his eyes tight on her face. How long had he been watching her? Still, it didn't matter. After the next minute or two he would realise he had been chasing an illusion, someone who hadn't existed. 'I need to talk to you,' she said flatly.

'I'm all ears.' The habitual mask that so very rarely lifted from his hard features had slid into place at her words, but behind it his mind was racing. What the hell was she going to say? From the look on her face for the last few minutes he wasn't going to like it, and he'd been so close to breaking through. Damn it, she was beautiful. His body ached with her beauty...

'What nearly happened...' She took a deep breath, embarrassment and pain constricting her throat, and swallowed hard before continuing. 'It was a mistake—on my side, I mean.'

'Was it?' His voice was cool now, cool and contained, and already he was making her feel small. 'You seemed to be there with me, if I remember.'

'Yes, I was.' She raised her head a little higher and stared him straight in the face, a spark of anger putting welcome adrenalin where she needed it. 'But it was still a mistake. I don't want an affair with you, Colt—'

'Oh, not that again—'

'I don't.' She cut into his drawl before he could say

any more. 'I can't blame what happened on you; you've made it perfectly clear from day one exactly where you stand.'

He said nothing now, watching her with narrowed, hooded eyes, his face so cold she knew she couldn't say it all. She just didn't have the courage.

'But contrary to what you might believe I don't jump into bed with all my boyfriends, not until...'

'Until?' he asked softly.

'Until it's right,' she said desperately. 'There has to be some commitment, something more than mere physical desire.'

'At the risk of being indelicate, that didn't seem to work out too well with your ex-fiancé, did it?' He raised a sardonic black eyebrow. 'I trust the faithless William *did* convince you of his love and loyalty before you agreed to wed him?'

'I don't think he could have,' she said slowly, a faint note of bewilderment in her voice now as she considered what he had asked. 'I never wanted to sleep with him before we were married anyway; I... He didn't push that side of things, and I didn't want it.'

'A match made in heaven.' The cynicism was cutting, and she didn't have the experience to realise it was partly a defence mechanism. 'You should have stuck to one of your former swains, it would seem.'

'Put it your own way.' The adrenalin was back, stronger now. 'But that's how it was.'

'So you are saying you want security in payment for your body; is that it?' he asked derisively. 'Followed through to its logical conclusion, doesn't that bear a marked resemblance to the oldest profession in the world?'

'I'm not saying I want payment,' she said hotly, furious at his deliberate twisting of her words. 'I'm saying there has to be commitment, trust, understanding...love.'

'Love?' His bark of a laugh held no amusement whatsoever. 'Oh, come on, Jessica, be real. What place does love have in the world in which we live? It's an illusion, a figment of the imagination. Women have been persuading the male sex for years that such a thing exists, merely to sweeten and make more acceptable the natural biological urge to mate. Open your eyes, look around you.'

'I have, and I'm not just seeing what I want to see,' she said tightly.

'Meaning I do?' He settled further back in the chair, eyeing her through narrowed grey slits of glittering light. 'Love is the biggest con trick out; you of all people should know that. Look at William and this sister of yours—you thought they loved you, didn't you? And your parents—sixteen years together and then your mother leaves him for someone else. Was this other guy younger, richer, or just more exciting, eh? There must have been something—'

'My mother still loves my father.' She was infinitely grateful that the recent conversation with her mother had taken place. 'She's always loved him; she loves him so much she finds it difficult to share him, and in the end that was too painful,' she said tightly.

'Share him?' He straightened a little but his face was expressionless. 'What does that mean?'

'With his work,' she said flatly. 'My father is one of those men who is consumed by his work; it leaves little room for anything else. My mother thought she could handle it, but she couldn't.'

'She told you that?' he drawled mockingly.

The indication was clear and now she rose slowly from the table, pushing back her chair as she gave him a long, level look. 'I'd like to go home, please,' she said flatly.

'Okay, so you want commitment.' He didn't move a muscle. 'How about an apartment of your own? A bank account? A written contract, if you like? Just tell me, and it's yours.'

'I don't believe you just said that.' She stared at him,

her revulsion clear, and he rose swiftly—so swiftly that his chair went skidding back against the wall with a clatter neither of them heard as they faced each other like two gladiators about to do battle.

'Damn it, Jessica, what do you want from me?' he ground out savagely, dull red searing the high cheek-bones and turning his eyes into jet-black stone. 'I can understand you want a home of your own, somewhere to put down roots after the unsettled childhood you had, being moved from place to place, and I'm willing to arrange that. The desire is natural, especially for a woman—'

'Don't patronise me, Colt.' This was hurting, hurting far more than she had expected. What did she want from him? She wanted it all—commitment, love, marriage, children. 'I don't want anything from you, I've told you,' she said as calmly as she could.

'You're lying.'

'Is it so impossible for the great Colt Irons to believe that he's being turned down?' she asked bitterly, using the words as much to fight her overwhelming desire to fall into his arms, to agree to be his until he tired of her, found a new distraction, as to fight Colt himself.

And she had to fight it. Those brief glimpses he had allowed her of the real man were too seductive, too sweet. If she became his lover then by the very order of things she would see that other side more and more, and when it was time for her to go it would destroy her. She thought she had been to hell and back on her wedding day, and in the ensuing months, but that would seem like a holiday compared to what Colt Irons could do to her.

'Is that how you see me, Jessica? As some sort of macho man whose brain is situated a good deal lower than his head?' he asked icily. 'In spite of all I've said?'

'You haven't *said* anything,' she protested quietly, her voice flat as the realisation that they were talking on different wavelengths swept over her. It must have been terrible for him to lose his fiancée so cruelly, but the bitterness and iron-hard resolve not to get involved again were not normal by any standards, and the hate he had displayed towards his sister... She didn't understand him; she didn't understand the first thing about this man. And yet she loved him beyond life. And it was love that now prompted her to say, 'Why, Colt? Why the fear of getting involved?'

'Fear?' She saw him bristle at the word and knew she had hit him on the raw. 'Don't try some amateur psychoanalysis, Jessica, just because we see things differently.'

'William let me down just about as badly as anyone could, but if I met the right man—' if he would lower those steel defences '—I'd be prepared to try again,' she said quietly.

'But I'm not that man.'

She hadn't meant it like that, she thought desperately as she saw his mouth tighten. 'I'm trying to say it has to be right—'

'Really?' He cut into her explanation with a perfectly calm voice that fooled her as he moved into the space between them. But then his intention became clear as he took her in his arms, drawing her into the urgent hardness of his body as his mouth covered hers hungrily.

On their arrival at his apartment he had discarded his light suit jacket, and now she could feel his heart thudding against the wall of his chest through the thin silk shirt, the delicious smell and feel of him inciting the madness that always sprang into play the second he touched her. She knew he didn't love her, knew that word was alien to his concept of the man/woman relationship, but when he was as close as this it ceased to matter.

He used all his experience, his hands and mouth working in seductive harmony, and she could no more have fought him than flown to the moon. One moment he was gentle and tender, the next he was fiercely possessive, with a sensuality that caused molten fire to flow through her veins, his technique changing moment by moment in a clear assault to bring her to capitulation.

She wasn't aware of the moment when he lowered her to the deep, thick, soft pile of the carpet, the desire that had saturated her being red-hot and shatteringly fluid. But she opened her eyes a moment or two later as the knowledge that he wasn't caressing her any more, merely holding her close, registered.

'This is right, Jessica; make no mistake about that.' His eyes had been waiting for her and as she stared dazedly at him he put her from him, rising lazily to his feet to stand looking down at her, his face enigmatic. 'And deep inside that beautiful, stubborn head of yours you know it. But until you're ready to admit it to yourself I can be patient. I've no intention of letting you pretend to yourself that I've taken you against your will. When I possess you it will be with the full consent of your mind and your body.'

He had stopped? She continued to gaze up at him for a second longer before realising the state of her undress, and then, as her cheeks flamed, she fumbled hastily with her clothes. *How could he?* The last few minutes had been an exercise in proving to her that he could have her any time he wanted, and also that he was calling the tune. Her mind went numb with disbelief.

'I never want to see you again,' she said with a painful flatness that caused his mouth to tighten. But when she rose to her feet and glanced his way the dark face was expressionless and cool. 'I mean it, Colt.'

'Now you are being childish,' he said with distant frostiness, the passionate lover of minutes before utterly gone and the cold, tyrannical millionaire who ruled his small empire with absolute power very much in evidence.

'No, merely truthful.' There was a sick, cold feeling in the core of her that she didn't dare examine. The only way she could finish this dreadful evening with some dignity was to work on automatic. 'You've made your point; be content with that.'

'My point?' His voice was rasping now. 'What the hell does that mean?'

'Work it out for yourself.' She was too hurt and too demoralised to argue any further; all she wanted was to get home and shut the door on Colt and the rest of the world. First William and now him. What was it about her that caused men to be able to turn their feelings on and off so easily? Other women were loved, cherished, adored. Why was she so different?

And, whatever Colt said about love, he had loved once. He had cared so deeply and so fiercely that when his beloved had been snatched from him it had turned him into this block of stone. But no, not quite a block of stone. A block of stone would be easy to forget. But the tantalising glimpses of that old Colt that his fiancée must have known were just enough to let her know what she had missed.

'Jessica—'

'I want to go home.' It was the cry of a child and he recognised she was at the end of her tether, the hand that had reached out to her falling by his side as he stared at her for one more long moment before nodding abruptly.

'If that's what you want,' he said shortly, his voice cryptic and cool.

What she wanted? When did what she want have any bearing on anything? she thought bitterly, even as she inclined her head with an abruptness that matched his. 'Thank you.'

The drive home was a nightmare she wouldn't have wished on her worst enemy, and it didn't help to know that this was the last time she would be with him. She wouldn't ever, *ever* see him again because to see him meant being hurt by him and there was no way it could be any different.

She tried to hide her distress, keeping her eyes fixed on her lap, the soft, elegant lines of the dress as it fell against her shape adding their own mockery to the inner misery that held her in its grip. She had thought she was so clever, so in control, when she had bought this outfit this afternoon... This afternoon? Was it really just a few hours ago that she had had the temerity to think she could manage the proposed graceful exit from his life without a backward glance?

But she hadn't thought that, not really. Her eyes darkened with a mixture of self-contempt and pain as she admitted to herself that she had hoped—right up to the moment he had shown he could turn his attraction for her on and off like a tap—that he would forget his old ways and form a relationship. A relationship which, if not exactly on her terms, was one where some compromise could be reached. A softening, a possibility that she might just earn a place in his heart—that was what she had been hoping for. Fool, fool, fool. She bit her lip until she tasted blood in an effort not to moan out loud. Had there even been such a fool as she?

'I'll see you to your door.' His voice was cool and without expression as they drew up outside the house, and that in itself made her want to scream and shout and claw at his face until the blood flowed. How could she be feeling like this, so wretched, so utterly miserable, when he wasn't affected even the tiniest bit?

The furious outrage that flooded her system at the injustice of it all enabled her to turn to him, her face blank, as she said, with all the control she could muster, 'Please don't bother. And I meant what I said, Colt—I don't want to see you again.'

'One could say you were in danger of labouring the point, Jessica.'

The mocking note was the last straw.

'Yes, one could.' She had already opened the car door, one slender leg half out of the car, when she turned back to him, her eyes flashing and her face white. 'But then I'm not perfect like you, am I? I'm made of flesh and blood, and inconvenient though that might be at times,

I prefer it to being a block of ice like you! You dared, you actually dared, to challenge me in the garden of Harry's house all those weeks ago to start to live again. What was it you said? Oh, yes, I've got it—I mustn't lock myself away in an ivory tower. Ivory tower! I can't believe you could use those very words when your whole life is conducted way, way up in the clouds! If anyone doesn't live in the real world it's you, Colt Irons—'

'You're hysterical,' he interrupted coldly, but she could see she'd broken through that unbearable remoteness by the tightness of his mouth.

'Probably,' she agreed wildly. 'But, like I said, I'm human. Human, Colt. With all the irritating little characteristics you seem to despise so much—a desire to be loved, wanted, needed. And just because things have gone wrong once I'm not going to give up, unlike you.'

'I'd stop *now*, Jessica.' The dark, sensual face was as cold as ice. 'You know nothing about me.'

'I know your fiancée was killed, your sister too, and that's what's made you as you are today.' She took a breath to say more, but as the slate-grey eyes fastened fully on her face she saw the irises were black with rage and her vocal cords froze. She expected him to shout at her, to vent some of the black emotion evident in every line of his big, taut body. But as the silence stretched and vibrated she sensed he wouldn't allow himself to lose control—and again the sheer iron will, the power of that cold, analytical mind, made her despair. She would never reach him; she'd been mad to try.

'Goodbye.' She launched herself out of the car as she spoke, falling into the quiet London street in a flurry of limbs and coffee-coloured silk. She didn't hear his voice calling her back. There was just silence—a deep, forbidding silence that told her he was finished with her, that her last words had been an intrusion he would never forgive.

'I don't care, I don't...' She was half sobbing, half

muttering to herself as she climbed the stairs to her bed-sit, her heart pounding with an ache that threatened to stop it beating altogether. 'I only said the truth; he can't blame me for that.'

But he would. The thought slashed through her as she shut the door behind her. Oh, yes, he would. The scene she'd caused earlier combined with the accusations of the last hour or so meant she'd well and truly burnt all her boats. She closed her eyes and allowed herself to give in to the dark, rushing flood of misery that was washing over her head.

CHAPTER EIGHT

SUNDAY dawned in a sky of transparent eggshell-blue, the sun fiercely hot as it rose to its height, making the air heavy with myriad summer scents that brought out young girls in bright summer dresses and large straw hats.

Jessica awoke mid-morning after a restless, troubled night populated with half-formed dark dreams and nightmarish images that still hung around in the light of day. She made herself a strong cup of black coffee after opening the windows wide, taking it back to bed with her and lying quietly as the caffeine began its stimulating work on her somnolent senses.

Janie banged on her door just after eleven, her voice as eager and energetic as always. 'Jess? You're not still asleep, are you?'

'What is it?' Jessica padded across to the door and winced slightly as Janie bounded into the room, her slender body encased in a long, sleeveless pinafore dress of pink gingham that clashed alarmingly with her thick-curly red hair, and her small feet shod in a pair of clumsy black boots. But she looked good somehow, she always did, and the natural exuberance that was an essential part of the Scottish girl added to her charm.

'You've forgotten, haven't you? I knew you would.' Janie turned, pirouetting in a graceful movement that was all her own as she frowned Jessica's way. 'The picnic? All the house are going on a picnic. I *told* you.'

'Oh, yes, of course.' Jessica hesitated, wondering what she could say. She couldn't endure a picnic feeling the way she did; she'd ruin the day for the others. 'Janie, I don't think—'

'Oh, no, you aren't going to get out of it, Jess.' Janie clamped her small hands on her bony hips, her frown deepening. 'Is it man trouble?' she asked disarmingly.

'What?' Jessica stared at her in amazement.

'You've been up and down like a yo-yo the last few weeks, and in my experience a man is usually at the bottom of any trouble,' Janie stated with the maturity of her twenty-and-a-bit years. 'Well, is it?' she persisted.

'In a manner of speaking,' Jessica admitted quietly.

'Oh, Jess, my poor wee lass, you don't half pick 'em.' It was meant to be sympathetic but somehow, coming from Janie, it turned into something comical, and although Jessica wouldn't have believed she could smile this morning she found herself doing just that. 'Well, a day in the country is just what you need,' Janie stated firmly. 'Everyone's coming—Mick and Gerald from upstairs, Sarah and Brent, and that new lad, Derek, and me and you. It'll do you the world of good. Brent's boss has lent him his old Land Rover—that'll take all of us, so we won't be split into two cars.

'I'll give you ten minutes to get ready, okay? and bring any food you think's suitable. Everyone's bringing something, but no one knows what, so what sort of lunch we'll have is anyone's guess.'

Jessica opened her mouth to protest further and then, as Janie grinned her impish grin, shut it again. The other members of the house were a good-natured bunch, and it wasn't often they all managed a day out together. She couldn't be a spoilsport. 'I might not be good company,' she warned quietly.

'Oh, get on with you, now.' Janie danced to the door. 'You be just what you want to be. You don't have to put on a show for us lot; you know that.'

As it happened the day was therapeutic, in its own madcap way, full of crazy moments and laughter. And although Jessica was ever conscious of a dull ache in her heart region, and a greyness that even the kindness of good friends couldn't dispel, she acknowledged it was far better to be out with the others than moping at home.

An hour's drive took them to the beautiful little town of Henley-on-Thames, and they ate their hotch-potch of a lunch stretched out on the grassy banks of the river in the hot sunshine, washing it down with warm, cheap red wine from paper cups, which was Janie's contribution, before piling back in the Land Rover to venture further into the countryside.

After a couple of hours of tramping through daisy-covered meadows and clambering over broken-down styles, they downed ice-cold glasses of draught stout in the flower-festooned garden of a little village pub before making for home, tired and slightly sunburnt.

Jessica didn't join in the sing-song on the way back, but sat listening to the others as they sang rip-roaring ditties and current pop songs, wondering if she would ever again feel as carefree and happy as they so obviously did. All day long a certain tall, loose-limbed tycoon with cruel, handsome features and eyes the colour of a stormy sea had occupied her thoughts, try as she might to dismiss him from her mind. What had he been doing today? As the refrains of 'The Wild Rover' vibrated through the long, grubby vehicle she thought of the immaculate Ferrari that was so at variance with the old Land Rover.

Had Colt ever bumped around in an ancient four-wheel drive with a group of friends? Drunk tepid wine out of paper cups? Been with people who didn't want anything from him, didn't care if he was rich or poor? She'd never know, would she? Perhaps he had, in his university days, before everything had soured and turned bad...

Oh, she had to stop thinking like this, had to put him out of her mind. The brief Colt Irons episode in her life *had* to be viewed as an experience, that was all.

She turned abruptly, with a little shake of her blonde head, to gaze out of the none too clean window, the lazy summer evening outside seeming to mock her pain and confusion.

Did everyone talk such rubbish to themselves? she asked herself caustically as the large vehicle rattled on. She would never forget Colt—he wasn't the sort of man who could be slotted away in a little box labelled 'the past.' The best she could hope for was that eventually, with the passage of time, she wouldn't have his dark, handsome face in front of her every other minute. Wouldn't wonder, with such searing intensity, who he was with or what he was doing... Hot tears pricked the back of her eyes and she blinked them away fiercely, horrified she might break down in front of the others.

Once back at the house she refused the invitation to join Janie and a couple of the others for a pizza and escaped to her room, where she had two big mugs of strong black coffee and gave herself a stern talking-to before popping downstairs and ringing Russell's number. He answered immediately, a lilt in his voice that told her the news was good. 'A perfect little boy, Jess; I can't believe it. He's got more hair than me!'

'And Monica's okay?' Jessica asked, smiling in spite of herself at his obvious delight.

'She's fine—exhausted but fine. We were sorry to miss the night out with Colt but he made it clear he's taken a rain check, so all is not lost. Did it go well?' Russell asked innocently.

She said what she knew he wanted to hear, and put the phone down a few minutes later with great relief. She hated lying, and she wasn't very good at it at the best of times—which this wasn't—but she couldn't have spoilt this special weekend for Russell by telling him the bald truth, she thought miserably. He had been so thrilled about his son and on such a mental high.

She went back upstairs and stood for long minutes under the shower, letting the flow of warm, silky water wash away the dust of the day, before returning to her room and getting straight into bed.

She didn't expect to sleep—the night was over-warm with a humid heat that was uncomfortable, and her mind was churning—but, to her surprise, she must have drifted off almost immediately because the next thing she knew the alarm was ringing loudly next to her ear.

She was still in her short towelling bathrobe, busy fixing a light breakfast of toast and coffee, her hair a mass of tousled silk about her slender shoulders, when she heard the telephone ring in the hall downstairs, and within moments Janie was banging at her door. 'It's your aunt, Carol's mother,' Janie said quickly as she opened the door. 'She wants to speak to you urgently; there's some sort of problem from the tone of her voice.'

Jessica flew downstairs, Janie disappearing back to her own room, and lifted the receiver with a sudden feeling of doom.

'Jess?' Her aunt's voice was stiff with the sort of controlled tightness that hid panic and horror and fear. 'I've some bad news, I'm afraid, but I knew you'd want to know. It's Carol—there's…there's been an accident, dear.'

'How badly is she hurt?' Jessica whispered weakly, her heart pounding.

'We aren't sure yet; she's in Intensive Care.' There was a screaming moment of silence before she continued, 'She's unconscious, Jess, but they're hoping she'll come round today—' A muffled sob came over the line and the next second her uncle spoke, his voice gruff.

'Hello, love. Look, we don't know too much at the moment, but your aunty insisted we call you.'

'I'm glad you did.' This couple had been like second parents to her since her return to England at eighteen, and she couldn't bear their pain. And Carol…poor, poor Carol… 'Shall I come down? Can I help?'

'No, love, no; you've got your job to think about.' But she knew by the way her uncle had hesitated that her aunt had been hoping she would do just that.

'I'll see you later,' she said firmly. 'I'm due some

holiday so I'll take a day now; Russell won't mind.' She
didn't care if he did or not, she thought silently. She was
going to Brindale come hell or high water.

'Look, please try not to worry,' she continued after a
moment, when her uncle didn't speak. His voice had
been suspiciously thick. Her words were ineffectual, and
she knew it, but there was little else to say. 'Does
Mother know—and…and Jo?' she asked carefully. It
hurt even now to say her sister's name.

'No, we've only called you, love. We've been sitting
by Carol's bed all night, but the doctor's sent us out to
the little day-room for sandwiches and coffee. I think
he's worried about your aunty; she's looking as though
she's going to drop.' She heard him gulp deep in his
throat and draw in a breath before he said, 'I've got to
go, Jess. We'll see you later, then? It's the Redmond
hospital, by the way.'

'All right, see you later. And please, give Aunty my
love.'

She stood in the quiet hall, her hand still on the phone
after she had replaced the receiver, listening to the muted
sounds of activity from the other rooms. *Carol.* Oh,
Carol. And she hadn't asked how it had happened—if
she'd been by herself—anything…

When the doorbell rang she didn't even consider the
fact that she was still in her bathrobe and her feet were
bare, walking to the end of the hall with leaden legs and
opening the heavy front door without asking who it was,
her eyes wide and dilated.

'Jessica?'

She wasn't even surprised Colt was standing on the
doorstep, but as the shock that had caused her to become
like an automaton also began to make her shake he took
in the situation with one glance. 'You know, then?
About Carol and Harry?'

'My aunt's just phoned me.' Her voice was distant,
remote to her ears, seeming to come from a long, long
way away. And as her vision clouded he stepped straight

into the hall, whisking her up in his arms before her legs gave way.

'What's going on?' Janie had reappeared, standing in the doorway to her room as Colt kicked the front door shut with his heel.

'She's had a shock. Where's her room?' he asked shortly, his voice crisp and brusque.

'First floor, first on the right.' As Colt moved swiftly to the stairs Janie called after him, 'Is there anything I can do?'

'No, I'll take care of her. Wait...have you got any brandy?'

'Yes, but—'

'Pour half a tumbler and bring it straight up; she's in shock.' He was taking the stairs two at a time as he spoke, in spite of Jessica's weight, and he didn't look back.

Janie stared after him for a few seconds, her eyes frankly appreciative, before turning to get the brandy. 'So that's him,' she muttered to herself as she sloshed it into a glass. 'Boy, oh boy, I can see why she's been like a cat on a hot tin roof. He's a darn sight dishier than that William creep.'

In the room upstairs the colour had begun to come back into Jessica's face by the time Janie brought the brandy. Colt dismissed the redhead with a polite but firm 'thank you', and shut the door behind her. Jessica sipped at it slowly with her eyes shut.

'How...how did you know?' she asked weakly after a full minute had ticked by, opening her eyes to see him kneeling just in front of her. She was more glad of the sustaining power of the brandy in that moment than in any that had gone before. He looked so big and dark, and so, so handsome as he crouched by her chair, his eyes narrowed and intent and his cruel mouth almost tender.

'I was due to have a meeting with Lord Brindale this morning and he rang me to explain about Harry. They've been at the hospital for most of the night,' Colt said softly, tilting the glass to her lips again with a gentleness that made her heart twist.

'Harry?' Colt's opening words came back to her. 'He's hurt too?' she asked anxiously. 'Do you know what happened?'

'It appears they were out for the day together yesterday,' Colt said slowly, straightening back on his heels and raking his hand through his hair in that gesture which she had begun to recognise meant he was agitated. 'Someone saw their car in a ditch some time after midnight and rang the police; that was the first anyone knew of the accident. According to Lord Brindale, Harry told him this morning that there had been sheep on the road and he'd swerved to avoid them and lost control of the car.'

'Harry's all right, then?' Jessica asked quietly, not daring to ask for the full facts about Carol.

'A broken leg and a touch of concussion,' Colt said shortly. 'It seems…it seems they hit a tree. The passenger side of the car took most of the impact and they were both trapped in the wreckage.'

'Carol.' Her voice was a whimper, and the next moment she buried her head in her hands as she wailed out loud, the brandy glass dropping to the floor where the remainder of the contents spilled out over the carpet like stale blood.

'She's going to be all right.' His voice was thick and husky and she wasn't aware of his hesitation before he stood up and pulled her into his arms, cradling her to him as she moaned her grief out loud. 'Stop it, Jessica; she'll be all right, I tell you,' he said softly. 'Don't upset yourself like this.'

'You don't know that.' She could barely speak through her tears. 'You don't know she'll be all right.'

'I do. Trust me. You need to be strong now—for Carol, for your aunt and uncle—'

'I'm tired of being strong.' It was a cry wrenched from

the very core of her, the misery and pain of the last seven months culminating in this moment of truth. And he folded her into him as they stood, slightly swaying, in the middle of the room.

'Shh, shh, my little one; no more tears, now.' His voice was soft and incredibly tender, more gentle than she would ever have dreamed it could be, his broad, masculine strength wonderfully protective. 'You've been brave, very brave; don't give up. Come on; come on.'

Quite when his wish to give comfort and her need to receive it became something more Jessica wasn't sure, but by the time her short robe fell open, displaying the silky curves and valleys of her body, she was locked in his arms. She clung to him unashamedly, giving him back kiss for kiss as their passion mounted. She'd thought she'd lost him; she'd imagined she'd never see him again... Those two thoughts pounded in her head as she whispered his name over and over again in an agony of love, her fear and distress giving a deeper poignancy to the moment.

'Jessica, you don't know what you're doing to me...' It was a warning, his voice thick and hoarse, his control brittle. 'I came to help.'

As he made to move away, she moaned softly in the back of her throat, the sound primitive and sensual, and he shuddered in reaction as her fingers tightened in the hair on the back of his head. 'No, don't leave me. I love you.' It was a barely coherent whisper against the side of his mouth as her lips searched for his, her eyes shut and her whole being wrapped in the feel and smell of him to the point where nothing else was real.

She wasn't aware of the colour leaving his countenance or the way his eyes snapped to her upturned face. But when, in the next instant, she found herself thrust to one side, and not gently, the deluge of icy cold hurt and pain that flooded her system made her eyes open wide.

'Cover yourself.' His voice was hard and clipped and the sound went through her like a two-edged sword.

'What?' She hadn't realised the state of her undress, but now, as her shock and confusion caused her to take a step backwards, the open robe was evidence of her humiliation, and she stuttered and stammered as she said, 'I—I didn't... I th-thought you—'

'I came to see if you wanted to drive down to Brindale, that was all.' His words were like a slap in the face, and at her stricken expression he ground out, 'Hell, Jessica, I didn't mean it like that. You're upset, in shock; you aren't thinking straight—' He stopped abruptly, his mouth tightening as she wrenched the belt of the robe so fiercely that it looked as if it would cut her in two.

She had thrown herself at him. The words drummed in her head like a terrible refrain. And he had refused her...again. But this time there had been no harsh words beforehand, no barbed confrontation involving his will over hers. He had simply refused her.

She summoned up all the strength at her disposal, mental and physical, before forcing herself to speak in as normal a tone as possible. 'I'm sorry, Colt. I don't know how that happened.' Her dignity was both tangible and touching, and his mouth tightened still more as she continued, 'But I'll make my own way to Brindale, thank you.'

'Jessica—'

'Please leave now—'

'No.' The word was like a bullet, and the cruel, handsome face was hard, although his voice was softer as he went on, 'This is ridiculous, Jessica. You were upset, distraught; we both know that. It wasn't the moment for anything more. You know as well as I do that you would have regretted it bitterly if it had continued.'

He wasn't telling the whole truth. She stared at him as her face flamed with hot chagrin, and intuition born of her love for him gave her a discernment she could well have done without. He hadn't been thinking of her when he had rejected her so definitely—that wasn't the bottom line, she thought bitterly. She knew it without question. However he tried to dress it up, whatever interpretation he cared to put on it now, there was something more. There had been no question of his holding back until...

Oh, no. She shut her eyes for a split second. She hadn't. She hadn't said she loved him, had she? She couldn't have been so stupid. She almost whimpered again.

'I'm going down to Brindale to see Harry, you're going down to see Carol and your aunt and uncle—it would be idiotic not to travel together.' He frowned at her as she stood frozen in front of him. 'Surely you can see that?' he asked expressionlessly.

She had to salvage some shred of dignity from this awful mess and refusing to travel down with him wasn't the way, appealing though that easier option was at the moment, in view of her revelation. But perhaps he thought she hadn't meant it, that she had said it in the heat of the moment as a prelude to the lovemaking? she thought hopefully. She realised he was waiting for an answer and forced herself to speak.

'I suppose so.' Oh, how could she have revealed her feelings for him like that? she asked herself bitterly, the sick sensation increasing. She knew how he viewed any sort of emotional responsibility—he couldn't have made it clearer from the word go—but she had been so distraught over Carol, and so pleased to see him... *Fool, fool, fool.*

She continued to call herself every name under the sun as she quickly got ready, her stomach doing cartwheels as she relived the moments in his arms over and over until her head was spinning. Once he had obtained her agreement Colt had disappeared outside to the car, and the knowledge that he was waiting for her, added to the gnawing anxiety about Carol, was making her feel physically ill.

She didn't bother with any make-up and just gave her hair a quick brush without even looking in the mirror, the soft, feathery style she had invested in for the disastrous evening with Colt falling obediently into shape without any persuasion.

On leaving her room she sped downstairs to the telephone in the hall, calling her mother first and praying she hadn't already left for the part-time job she had. Mrs Taylor answered immediately, her voice slightly impatient, which probably meant she was late.

'Mum? It's Jessica.' She launched straight into an explanation, and by the time she'd finished there was a distinct sniffling at the other end of the phone, although her mother hadn't spoken. 'So I'm going down there with…a friend this morning,' Jessica added after a short pause. 'I'll let you know how things are.'

'A friend?' Her mother's voice was weak but curious. 'Male or female friend?'

'Male.' She could sense the maternal antennae beginning to buzz, and finished the call quickly before her mother could ask pertinent questions. She was too upset, and too raw, for the sort of conversation that might develop.

The phone call to Russell wasn't any easier. 'You're going down there with *Colt Irons*?' Whether it was Russell's recent elevation to fatherhood or not she didn't know, but there was a distinctly concerned note to her boss's sombre tones. 'How did that come about? You said you only found out about Carol first thing this morning.'

'I did.' She took a deep breath and decided to take the bull by the horns. 'And Colt didn't sleep at my place, if that's what you're thinking, Russell. He happens to know the other person who was injured—Harry Brindale. He's Lord Brindale's son, and Carol is going out with him.'

'I see.' He didn't, and it showed. 'It's just that…' There was an uncomfortable pause. 'Colt Irons has got something of a reputation where the ladies are concerned—love 'em and leave 'em, you know? I wouldn't want you to get hurt, Jess.'

His warning had come too late—far, far too late—but she had no intention of telling him so. 'Thanks, Russell,' she said quietly. 'But I'm going to Brindale purely to see Carol and that is all. I'll see you tomorrow morning as usual, all being well, but if there's any change I'll phone you tonight, okay? Monica and the baby still doing well?' The digression was successful and after a few moments of listening to Russell's rapturous description of his son she was able to replace the receiver without further mention of Colt.

He was staring straight ahead through the windscreen, his dark face grim and tense, as she left the house, but the moment she approached the car he leant across and opened her door for her, his eyes shooting to her pale face. 'Okay? How are you feeling?' he asked softly.

She knew his solicitude was owing to her shock and anxiety over Carol but she still flushed a deep scarlet as she slid into the car, the memory of those last few moments in his arms stark and humiliatingly clear. 'I'm fine, thank you. I just want to get to Brindale and find out exactly what's what now.'

'Of course.' The tenderness in his eyes was just her imagination—of course it was, she told herself sharply as she fumbled with her seat belt, her eyes misting with stupid tears. *Pull yourself together.* 'Do you need to make any calls before we leave London?' he asked gently.

'No, I've done all that.' Stop being so thoughtful, so kind, she told him silently as he started the powerful engine. Can't you see it's killing me? I don't want a taste of what could have been, if you'd been different, if I had...

The summer day was cool and overcast in stark contrast to the blazing hot sunshine of the day before, but the grey sky and chilly breeze seemed fitting somehow, in view of the reason for their journey. They left London in deep silence, Colt occupied with the heavy morning traffic and Jessica lost in her thoughts, tense and miserable. But once they were on the open road the atmosphere in the car became electric. She was vitally aware of every tiny movement he made, of his large, capable hands on the steering wheel, the powerful muscled thighs and long, long legs. He was so sure of himself, so in control, so…untouchable.

'Carol's very dear to you, isn't she?' The deep voice caused her to give a visible start, and she was glad his eyes were on the road and not on her.

'Yes, she is.' She took a deep breath and forced herself to continue talking, to give some semblance of normality to a situation that was anything but normal. 'She's more of a sister than a cousin; she always has been. Even before my parents split up we were close in a way that Jo and I never were—in spite of the fact that we only saw each other a few times a year, owing to my father's work. But we wrote to each other all the time, and phoned.

'After the divorce Carol and her parents were very supportive to Dad and me. It didn't make any difference that it was my aunt and mother who were sisters; they never took sides. When I came back to England to go to university I didn't want to live with my mother and Jo…' She paused, remembering how raw her feelings had been at that time. 'So my aunt and uncle made a home for me in the holidays. Carol's a darling, she really is, you know,' she added suddenly, turning to him with eyes darkened by pain.

'You care too much, you know that, don't you?' he said flatly, glancing at her for a moment with narrowed, veiled eyes.

Her heart gave a painful jerk. She really didn't know if he was referring to Carol or the fact that she had revealed she loved him, but it was easier to take the safer option. 'Carol loves me too; I know that,' she said quietly as her cheeks burnt hotly. 'If our positions were reversed she'd be on her way to see me now.'

'I don't doubt it,' he said.

She turned to stare at the hard, grim profile but he didn't glance her way again and she could read nothing from the cool mask of a face. She didn't understand him—even this conversation was a minefield of uncertainty, she thought bleakly. Why, oh, why had she gone and fallen for Colt Irons, of all people? There were hundreds, *thousands* of men out there who wanted a close, loving relationship with one woman, who thought commitment and monogamy were normal. Why hadn't she fallen for one of them?

She was no nearer the answer when they drew up outside the hospital some time later.

Her uncle was waiting for her in a small anteroom when they reached the ward and he made no effort to hide his displeasure when she introduced Colt.

'Mr Evans?' Colt's face was grave as he shook her uncle's hand. 'I'm very sorry we're meeting in such unfortunate circumstances. Is there any news?'

'Carol's regained consciousness,' the older man said stiffly, his face mellowing slightly as Jessica gave a sigh of relief and fell into his arms. 'She's going to be all right,' he added over Jessica's head, his eyes direct as they fastened on Colt's.

'That's good,' Colt said carefully.

'Yes, it is. She's very dear to me and she's been through more than enough lately.' The voice was bland, the eyes were anything but as they sent a message Colt couldn't mistake. 'I don't want her hurt.' He wasn't talking about Carol and they both knew it.

'None of us do.' Jessica hugged her uncle one more time before she stepped back a pace, totally oblivious to the undercurrents and taking her uncle's words purely at face value.

'No, of course we don't, love.' Her uncle nodded at her, his eyes warm as they fastened on her pale face.

'I'm sorry we've worried you like this, but your aunt was desperate to see you this morning.'

'Don't be silly; I'd have been mad if you hadn't rung and told me,' Jessica said quickly, standing on tiptoe to kiss his cheek. She wasn't aware of Colt watching the little interplay with cool, narrowed eyes but her uncle was, and the look he gave the younger man as they all moved to sit down wasn't warm. 'Colt's a friend of Harry's,' Jessica explained after a long pause when no one spoke. 'He was coming down to see him, so he gave me a lift.'

'I see.' Mr Evans' face was a study in blankness as he added, 'Just a friend of Harry's?'

'I've only met Carol once or twice,' Colt said pleasantly, his voice smooth as he parried the obvious question with a silky ease that did nothing to soften the older man's features.

Colt said nothing more for the remainder of the time before Jessica's aunt joined them, settling back in his seat with his arms crossed and one leg folded across his knee, his handsome face remote and cold and his eyes hooded. But once Mrs Evans had joined them, and after consultation with the hospital staff, it was decided that Jessica and Colt would return later that afternoon. Both patients were quite heavily sedated and sleeping, and there seemed little point in hanging around the clinical corridors of the hospital all day.

Except... Jessica kept her eyes cast down as her thoughts raced. A day spent in Colt's company after the fiasco of that morning was going to be embarrassing at best, painful at worst.

'Come home and have some lunch with us.' Mrs Evans leant across her husband and took one of Jessica's hands in hers. 'I want you to, darling. Would a salad and cold meat do?' she asked Colt now, turning her head in his direction as she still held onto Jessica's hand and giving him a beaming smile.

'You ought to go home and get some sleep,' Jessica

replied quickly before Colt could speak. She knew her
aunt of old and there was a definite matchmaking gleam
in her eye which couldn't have been more misplaced in
the circumstances.

'Oh, don't be silly.' Her aunt settled back in her seat,
flapping her hand. 'Now I know Carol is going to be all
right I'm fine. I might have a nap after lunch, anyway.
So…you follow us home, yes?' Again she turned to Colt
and this time he spoke before Jessica could open her
mouth.

'Thank you, Mrs Evans.' He gave the older woman
one of his devastating smiles that he used rarely, but
always to great effect. 'That's very kind of you.'

'It was kind of you to bring Jessica down so
promptly.' Mrs Evans was clearly hooked and ignored
the dark glare her husband gave her.

'He was coming down to see Harry anyway, Mabel,'
Mr Evans said stiffly after the little silence that followed.

Well, her uncle clearly wasn't enamoured with Colt,
Jessica thought ruefully, slanting a glance at the older
man from under her eyelashes. She remembered his
comments that first weekend she had met Colt, and shut
her eyes for a split second as apprehension about the
next few hours caused her stomach to turn over.

As it was, her uncle, as host, kept his feelings to himself and the next hour or two passed in relative harmony,
although Jessica wanted to curl up and die when her aunt
produced the inevitable photo album for Colt's perusal
just after lunch.

'Here's Jess when she was five; isn't she a little pet?'
Mrs Evans gushed as she pointed out a slender waif of
a child holding onto a rotund little Carol's hand.

'She's beautiful.' Colt's voice was very soft and very
deep, his eyes rising from the photograph to Jessica's
pink face before returning to the snapshots.

'And here she is with her parents, and this one was
taken in the first term of university, and here… Oh, I'm
sorry, Jess, I didn't know I'd kept that one after…' Mrs

Evans' voice died away in embarrassment as she tried unsuccessfully to remove a picture of a laughing Jessica wrapped in the arms of a tall blond man.

'It's all right, Aunty, really,' Jessica said softly. 'This is William,' she added to Colt, whose eyes were tight on her face. 'It was taken when we got engaged.'

'Jess, I'm sorry.' Her aunt was crushed, and Jessica moved from her big easy chair to the sofa where her aunt and Colt were sitting to give her a quick hug.

'Don't be silly; it doesn't matter.' There was a ring of genuineness in her voice that wasn't lost on any of the listeners. 'That's the past. I'm going forward now, and I know William wasn't right for me. I've seen some photographs of their little girl and she's beautiful. Have you seen her?' she added matter-of-factly.

'Their child?' Colt cut in before her aunt could reply, his voice sharp. 'They've had the baby?'

'Yes.' She turned to him now, her brown eyes open and direct. 'Life goes on, doesn't it?'

Her aunt spoke in the next instant and the conversation resumed less dangerous ground, although she was conscious of Colt's gaze lingering on the photograph of her and William for some moments before he turned the page.

'This is my sister.' Jessica kept her voice perfectly normal as she pointed out the photograph of Carol and herself, with another girl laughing in between them. 'Can you see the family resemblance?'

'No, I don't think she is in the least like you,' Colt said coolly, his rapier-sharp gaze dissecting the pointed, cat-like face in the photograph. 'Not in the least.'

'Neither do I.' It appeared that for once Colt and her uncle were in agreement. 'Josephine is an alley-cat against Jess's Persian,' he stated surprisingly.

'Michael!'

'Uncle!'

As both women stared, aghast, at him, Mr Evans nodded slowly. 'Oh, I'm right, I'm right. You might not like to admit it, but I'm right.'

'I'm sure you are, Mr Evans.' Colt's voice was smooth, with that slight thread of amusement that told Jessica he thoroughly appreciated her uncle's candour. 'It's amazing how different siblings can be.'

'Too true.' Her uncle was warming to the theme and after a horrified glance at Jessica her aunt rose swiftly, almost snatching the photo album out of Colt's hands at the same time as the doorbell rang imperiously.

'Oh, no, not another neighbour enquiring after Carol?' Mrs Evans gestured to her husband wearily to answer the door. They had had several enquiries during lunch, and although the concern was appreciated it was also tiring. 'I think I'll go and take that nap now,' she said quickly as they heard voices in the hall.

'Aunt Mabel...' The voice was dramatic and so was the posture of the girl standing framed in the doorway to the lounge, her arms stretched out theatrically and her small, feline face exactly like the photograph. 'Mother rang me this morning and I just had to come. Poor, poor Carol; it must be devastating for you. If you've never had a child you couldn't understand the love you feel, could you...? Oh, Jess!' Jo clapped a hand to her mouth as though she had just become aware of both her sister and her own tactlessness. 'I didn't see you; I thought you'd be at the hospital.'

'Hello, Jo.' Jessica didn't smile at her sister, knowing without a doubt that both the entrance and the words had been stage-managed for her benefit. And when Colt moved swiftly to her side, his hand sliding under her elbow as he moved her into his bulk, she was immensely glad of the support. 'How are you?'

'Fine, fine.' There wasn't a shred of remorse in the slanted hazel eyes, the green in them accentuating the impression of feline power as they moved slowly to Colt's dark face. 'Aren't you going to introduce us?'

So that was what it was all about, Jessica thought

numbly. Her mother had obviously mentioned that she was driving down with a man friend and Jo hadn't been able to resist seeing how the land lay. The excuse about Carol was transparent to anyone who knew the two girls—they had never been able to take each other's company even when they were little, and when Jo had run off with William Carol had made it clear she never wanted to see her cousin again. 'Colt, this is my sister, Jo. Jo, Colt Irons.'

'Hello.' Jo smiled prettily, showing little sharp white teeth, her eyes frankly predatory as they stroked over Colt's hard features. 'So you're a friend of Jess's?'

She was unbelievable, she really was absolutely unbelievable, Jessica thought helplessly as the shock that had numbed her mind and body at her sister's entrance began to diminish. Jo was looking up at Colt as though he was the best thing since sliced bread, almost licking her lips as she fluttered her eyelashes and flicked back her long, sleek blonde hair. Jessica could remember her eyeing William in the same way, but she hadn't thought anything of it at the time. Jo had never been able to resist trying to charm every man she came into contact with, and although she wasn't exactly beautiful there was a sensual attractiveness about her sister that had made her never short of a boyfriend.

'Yes, I am.' There was something in Colt's steely gaze that caused Jo's confidence to falter just for a moment, but then she smoothed her leggings over her hips with a little arching smile.

'How nice.'

'Is…is William with you?' Her aunt was clearly out of her depth but her uncle hadn't moved from his place in the doorway behind Jo, his gaze murderous as he glared at the back of her head.

'No.' The green-flecked eyes flickered and Jessica knew instantly that William had refused to come to save her further embarrassment. 'It was too long a journey for the baby. William thought it best to stay with her.

He's *such* a devoted father,' she cooed innocently, glancing in Jessica's direction. 'The world revolves around Caroline; he won't leave her for a minute.'

'That must make for an exciting lifestyle.' Colt's voice was lazy, his voice mildly playful as though he was making a joke, but as Jo's eyes flashed to his face Jessica saw he had hit her sister on the raw. She's already bored, Jessica thought in amazement. Bored and restless. And something Carol had said when she had first found out about William and Jo came back to her.

'It will be a marriage made in hell,' Carol had stated shrewdly. 'You mark my words, Jess; he'll rue the day he let you go.'

'Well, you know how it is.' Jo shrugged, obviously a little unsure of where Colt was coming from, although her overwhelming belief in her attractiveness to the opposite sex wouldn't let her acknowledge that Colt was less than enamoured by her charms.

'Not really.' Colt smiled, a cruel barracuda kind of smile. 'I'm used to successful career women like Jessica, who juggle their jobs and their hectic social lives with amazing aplomb and manage to stay cool and beautiful whatever the situation. Mind you, Jessica is undeniably special. But then I don't have to tell you that, do I?' he added silkily.

'I… No. No, she's…' For the first time that she could remember Jessica saw her sister lost for words. But she recovered almost instantly, her eyes narrowing into slits of green as she recognised that here was one man who could see her for exactly what she was.

The next hour was something of a revelation to Jessica. Twice more Jo was stupid enough to try and put her down and each time Colt smoothly turned things round with a merciless disregard for her sister's feelings.

By the time Jo left—her uncle having made it crystal-clear that Carol would not want to see her—Jessica was actually feeling sorry for her sister, especially when they saw her to the door and Jo realised the Ferrari parked just down the street was Colt's. Before William, Jo had made a career of dating men with big, expensive cars and big wallets to match. And now her face was green with envy as she glanced at Jessica, held close in the crook of Colt's arm, before raising her eyes to Colt.

'You're obviously very successful,' she said tightly, her voice feline with bitterness.

'I get by.' Colt smiled, his eyes as cold as ice as he watched the jealousy flash, dark and ugly, across the pretty, cat-like features. 'But wealth is relative, isn't it? What can compare to a happy marriage with the man you love, and a child to boot? I know they're a responsibility, a tie—but if you're happy that's nothing, is it?'

Jo had learnt enough in the last hour not to cross swords with him again and she merely inclined her head with a sharp little nod, although her face was venomous as she walked towards her own small family saloon.

'Poor William.' Colt's voice was reflective as they stood together in the doorway and watched Jo drive off without glancing in their direction again. 'It isn't often that retribution is so swift.'

'Colt?' She turned to him, putting her hand on his arm before they went back in to the others. 'Thank you for dealing with her like you did. I…I can't understand why she behaves like that. We were never great friends, even as children, but I thought she cared for me a little in her own strange way.'

'Jessica, every so often in a generation an accident of nature is born—someone who has nothing good in them, nothing of worth. They're incapable of finer feeling, self is all-important, and your sister is like that.'

'That's a bit harsh.' She looked at him, aghast.

'It's the truth. I dare say she's fooled your mother for years; mothers always want to believe the best of their children, even when it's almost impossible. But I've met others like Jo. Unfortunately she is not unique.'

She stared at him, the feeling that he was saying more than the mere words expressed strong again.

'Well, thank you anyway,' she said again. 'I…I was dreading the first time I saw her. But with Carol and everything I thought recriminations were out of place.'

'You're too nice.' He raised her chin as he spoke, his lips brushing hers in a fleeting kiss that held a peculiar kind of sweet sadness. 'Unlike me,' he added caustically as he moved a pace from her, thrusting his hands into his pockets as he glanced down the street to the Ferrari.

'I wouldn't say that.' She kept her voice light, but his eyes were narrowed and hard as his gaze returned to her.

'But you don't know me, Jessica,' he said coldly. The words were a rebuff and they hurt, but she forced herself to show no reaction as she stared back at him. For some reason he had withdrawn again, even more completely than before. What was it with him? she asked herself tightly as they walked back into the house. Talk about blowing hot and cold. No one could have protected her better than he had done that afternoon, but now he was the imperturbable ice-man again, and she was getting more than a little sick of his moods.

He was impossible to understand. As Colt made polite conversation with her aunt and uncle over a pot of tea, she found her mind was roaming elsewhere. She could understand that his fiancée's death had hurt him, but surely the years would have formed some scar tissue on the wound? And this animosity towards his sister, hate even; surely that was misplaced?

Oh… She gave herself a mental shake, her mind and body weary. She was too emotionally raw after the confrontation with Jo to think about all this any more, too bruised and sore.

They left for the hospital at just after four, arriving to find that Carol had been moved to a private room and that Harry was sitting by the side of her bed in a wheelchair, a blanket over his legs.

'Darling…' Mrs Evans flung herself on her daughter and after effusive greetings, and more than a few tears, order gradually reasserted itself—along with a gentle reminder from the sister, before she left, that 'Just a short visit, please' was the doctor's advice.

'You frightened us all to death.' Jessica smiled as she bent across the bed and kissed Carol's brow but her voice held a little tremor, and Carol hugged her close for a moment, her own lips trembling.

'No tears.' Harry's voice was brisk and despite the fact he was sitting in a wheelchair, his face white and bruised and the plaster cast of his left leg sticking out at an uncomfortable angle, his voice held a jaunty note that brought all eyes to him as he continued, 'Can I tell them?'

'Yes, go on.' Carol's face was tender as she smiled at the man holding her hand so tightly, and as Jessica straightened she found she had a lump in her throat at the way they were looking at each other.

'I've a little announcement.' Harry cleared his throat and looked up at them all as he said, 'I've asked Carol to be my wife, and she's done me the great honour of accepting—'

'*Darling!*' Mrs Evans' squeal of delight was followed by her bursting into tears, and in the ensuing pandemonium of hugs and kisses only Jessica noticed the change in Colt's body language that made his congratulations forced. But the coolness was there—oh, yes, it was there, she thought bewilderedly.

The next ten minutes were like ten hours, not because Jessica wasn't pleased for her cousin—she was, she was thrilled, she told herself silently. But she was so vitally aware of the big dark man sitting quietly at her side that it was painful. Colt had made the appropriate responses that fitted the occasion, his mouth smiling but the slate-grey eyes cold. It was almost as though they were a host of tiny insects under glass, she thought bitterly, being surveyed by a superior intelligence that regarded their activities with a patronising kind of pity.

'We really ought to go before that formidable sister comes back and throws us out.' She rose as she spoke, forcing a warm smile to her lips as she glanced at Carol and Harry. 'I'll phone tomorrow, if that's all right? And I'm pleased, so pleased.'

She bent to kiss her cousin goodbye, and Carol hugged her close with an urgency that belied her weak state. 'I do love you, Jess. You'll ring me tomorrow, then? I'm so glad you came.'

She knew what Carol was trying to say and her voice was gentle as she said, 'I'm really thrilled for you, Carol. And he's the one for you. You'd better make me number one bridesmaid.'

'I will, oh, I will.' They held each other close for a moment more and then Jessica straightened, a bright smile stitched to her face as she glanced round the room, looking everywhere but at Colt.

Goodbyes completed, they left. Without a word being spoken they stepped into the sterile corridor outside and walked through the hospital passageways until they emerged out of the plate-glass doors into the cool summer evening, fragrant with the tang of woodsmoke.

For some reason she couldn't explain to herself Jessica was angry—fiercely, furiously angry—the emotion consuming all the pain and hurt and confusion of the last few weeks in a blazing hot flood that had her quivering all over.

Everything, their whole relationship—such as it was—had been at his bidding. Oh, he'd been honest, stating the rules of play quite blatantly right from the first; she couldn't fault him on that. Her mouth tightened into a thin line as they walked to the car. But he had used every weapon at his disposal to get her into his bed—all the experience and finesse he had gained through the years, without a thought of how she was going to feel when it was over. He had assumed she was like all the others, and when she hadn't conformed exactly to the nice, neat little mould he'd had in mind it was her fault! Well, she loved him—and it wasn't her fault. No way.

She glared ahead as she slid into the car but instead of shutting her door he placed his hands on the roof of the car, bending down to stare at her as he said, 'Well? The waves are coming hot and strong.'

'Are they?' She spared him one scathing glance, her heart giving a painful squeeze as she took in his dark countenance, but then she willed herself not to falter.

'They surely are.' He eyed her thoughtfully. 'So what's wrong?' he asked quietly. 'What's upset you?'

'Do you have to ask?' She raised her head, meeting his eyes with her own. 'You could at least have pretended you were glad for them—they were announcing their engagement, for goodness' sake.'

'Carol and Harry?' He was genuinely surprised. 'I *am* glad for them.'

'Oh, sure.' She didn't know what had got into her, but she was aware she wasn't herself. Mind you, 'herself' hadn't been doing too well lately...

'Okay, spit it out.' His eyes had narrowed, the faint, misty drizzle that had begun to fall coating his black hair with a sheen that made it seem alive in the grey light. 'You're obviously spoiling for a fight,' he said grimly.

'Is that what you think?' How dared he stand there so nonchalantly, so casually, when she was turning inside out? she asked herself tightly. He might be rich and powerful and handsome—too handsome for his own good, the little voice in her head added nastily—but she was going to tell it as it was for once. He wouldn't want to hear it, she knew that, but she was sick of pussy-footing about with him.

Somehow the transparent happiness of Carol and Harry had touched something deep inside her with a poignancy that had hit her on the raw. It was *natural* to meet someone and fall in love, *natural* to want more than just a good time for a few short days or weeks, *natural* to care. He had made her feel as though she was less than nothing when she had told him how she felt, that she loved him, but it wasn't she who had the problem...

'You're telling me I'm wrong?' he asked sardonically.

'About me wanting a fight? Probably not,' she said tartly. 'But about everything else in your life? Dead right you are.'

'That's definitely fighting talk.' He was trying to give her the impression he was amused, she thought suddenly, with that dart of intuition that had served her more than once lately, but he wasn't. The narrowed brilliance of his eyes and the tightness of his smile spoke volumes.

He straightened, his muscled shoulders flexing under the thin silk of his shirt, and there was a pagan blackness to his hair as he strode round to his side of the car after slamming her door shut with slightly more force than was merited. No, he wasn't amused, she thought again as her nerves leapt at the coming confrontation, but then neither was she. This wasn't some sort of sophisticated game, however much he tried to make it so. She prepared herself for the onslaught that would follow.

Contrary to her expectation, however, he didn't launch into the attack as soon as he was seated, or indulge in the razor-sharp cynicism that was so devastating. He started the engine, checked his mirrors and then carefully eased the powerful car out of the hospital carpark, driving with a controlled authority that was an integral part of everything he did.

They drove for some minutes in a quietness that positively crackled, the soft swish of the windscreen wipers doing nothing to alleviate the tension. Jessica was just wondering whether to challenge him again—to say something, anything, to break the wall of silence—when he pulled off the road into a deserted picnic area, cutting the engine with a sharp turn of the ignition.

'You're mad at me, and I can understand that.'

It wasn't what she had expected him to say and she didn't know how to react—but then he reached for her, his mouth claiming hers with a furious need that sent her blood shooting through her veins, her body melting into his. The kiss was thorough and deep, his mouth drinking from hers, and she felt her senses begin to spiral into that strange half-world he always evoked, where the only things that were real and had any substance were his lips and hands and body.

'No…' She raised her hand to push him away but he caught her fingers, enclosing them in his own before he raised his head from hers. Her eyes were bright and dilated as he carefully spread her fingers against the palm of his hand before lowering his head as he turned her palm over, nuzzling at the base of her wrist with his lips and tongue, sending flames of desire pulsing through every vein.

'You're beautiful, Jessica, beautiful and warm and loving. Everything a man could want.' She was cradled into him, his body leaving hers in no doubt as to how she was affecting him, but there was something in his words, some intonation, that wasn't right. 'You'll make some man a wonderful wife one day.'

And then she understood, even before he carefully eased himself away, one hand lingering for a few seconds more in the rich silkiness of her hair before he turned completely into his seat and away from her.

It had been goodbye.

CHAPTER NINE

JESSICA sat for some seconds, her mind blank, before waves of pain and fury replaced the numbness. 'What was all that about?' she asked stiffly to Colt's grim profile. She knew, oh, she knew all right, but he could darn well spell it out, she thought bitterly. No more 'silent macho man'; she'd had enough.

'We'd better get on; a storm's forecast—'

'Blow the storm.' She was keeping control of her voice with all the will she possessed. He wasn't going to just dismiss her like this, act the cool, cultured man of the world who kept everything light and sophisticated. They were going to *talk*, really talk, whatever the result. The real Colt Irons was in there, buried deep under the layers of cosmopolitan worldliness, and she had caught enough glimpses of him over the last few weeks to know that he was quite different from Colt Irons the tycoon and multi-millionaire. 'I asked you a question,' she said quietly, 'and I want an answer.'

'Leave it, Jessica.' His voice was clipped.

'I can't.' Her chin rose a notch. 'I want to know how you can kiss me like that and then just turn away as though it doesn't mean anything.'

'It doesn't.' It was cruel and her face whitened. 'Your uncle understands. He doesn't like me, you know. I can't blame him. If I'd got an innocent little lamb I'd react the same way. He knows the sort of man I am.'

'He hasn't got a clue what sort of man you are.' Her voice was fierce and his gaze snapped to her before he ran his hand through his hair, shutting his eyes for an infinitesimal moment as though her instinctive defence of him had hurt.

'Don't do this, Jessica; it isn't going to help either of us,' he warned softly. 'You need a Harry Brindale type; I've never seen it so clearly as this afternoon. A 2.4 family man, who leaves at nine and returns at five and spends the weekend mowing the lawn—'

'Don't tell me what I need.' She'd never spoken in such a tone before, controlled and cool but with a firmness that was convincing. 'I know what I need.'

'And so do I. Someone fresh, young—'

'You're not old,' she protested quickly. 'Thirty-five isn't old.' And then she blushed scarlet as she realised what she'd said.

'I'm old in here, Jessica.' He tapped his head slowly. 'I became old in here at your age—' He stopped abruptly. 'But that's another story,' he said harshly. 'And one which I have no intention of burdening you with.'

'I want to know,' she said quietly, praying her voice wouldn't shake.

'No.' He shook his head, his voice cold. 'Damn it, woman, what the hell do you want, anyway? You've resisted all my efforts to get you into my bed, and now when I admit defeat—'

'It isn't like that and don't you dare try to bring it down to that level,' she spat angrily. Part of her couldn't believe she was doing this, couldn't believe she had so little self-respect that she was arguing with a man who had made it quite clear he was finished with her. But nothing was black and white where Colt was concerned; she felt that right in the core of her. What you saw was most definitely a clever illusion, and however much it hurt she wanted the truth. She said as much, her voice beginning to shake slightly. 'I want to know what you really think, feel—'

'Truth games?' His voice was scathing. 'I left all that behind a long time ago, Jessica.'

'You might have left the truth behind, but the games

still remain as far as I can see,' she bit out sharply, stung by his open contempt.

The grey eyes glittered dangerously and then narrowed into points of light that were laser-bright. 'Exactly. And you're a straightforward country wench at heart, aren't you?' he drawled silkily. 'The sort who bakes apple pies and home-made bread, and has a man's slippers waiting by the fire. We're poles apart, Jessica, I do agree—'

'I didn't say that.' She glared at him, her cheeks flushed and her mouth trembling despite all her efforts to remain calm. 'And I haven't the remotest idea how to make bread.'

'But you'd learn. For the man you loved, you'd learn,' he said quietly, as though it were the worst indictment in the world.

She drew in a sharp breath at the look on his face, utterly out of her depth. What was he saying? 'Is that bad?' she asked shakily, unable to deny it. For him she would learn to make bread and a million other things besides, she thought helplessly. He had to be one of the sexiest men in the world and she wanted him—physically very much, although there was more, much, much more to her feelings than that. She wanted all of him— his body, his mind, his heart—and she wanted to be everything to him.

'Bad? Not bad—certainly not for the 2.4 guy who wouldn't be able to believe his luck in getting a woman like you,' he said slowly. 'He'd be what you need— someone who would cherish you, look out for you, make it all hang together—'

'I know the sort of man you mean,' she said flatly, forcing all expression out of her voice as she continued. 'He would be the sort who would follow a woman out of a party, a woman who had just insulted him in the worst possible way, because she was crying and he was concerned about her. The sort who, if this woman accused him of trying to buy her and caused a scene, would give her the job anyway, the job he knew would mean such a boost to her career.

'He would drop everything and come round to see her when he suspected she might have received some bad news that would be hard to take, but do it in such a way that she wouldn't feel beholden to him. And, likewise, he wouldn't take her physically, even though he knew he could, because he didn't think she could cope emotionally afterwards. Is that the sort of man you mean, Colt?'

He was staring fixedly at her, his eyes still narrowed and his mouth tight with tension, and he had never looked so handsome—or so remote. She wasn't getting through...

'I know what sort of man you think you are,' she said quietly, willing him to understand what she was saying. 'But you've never been like that with me; don't you see?' Her velvet brown eyes darkened to onyx with a mixture of pain and desire. 'Even in the early days, that first night at the Brindales', you were concerned for me.'

'Don't make me into some sort of saint, Jessica,' he said harshly. 'I want women for one thing and one thing only, and I've never pretended differently.'

'I don't believe that.' She knelt on the seat, reaching out to him. 'I don't,' she said softly. 'I won't.'

'*Hell, woman, what are you trying to do to me?*' Just for a moment the iron control slipped and the mask was gone, his voice raw and ugly. 'You haven't the faintest idea of what I'm really like, the way I've lived over the last ten years. I've taken what I want and I've done it without regard for anyone or anything; that—*that* is the truth.'

'Then why didn't you take me?' she asked softly. 'You told me you wanted me.'

'Stop this.' He pushed against the steering wheel for a moment, his arms outstretched and his body taut, before relaxing back into the seat as he raked his hand through his hair. And then he turned to her, slowly, his mouth a thin line in the hard planes of his face. 'You want to know what makes me tick, Jessica? Do you? You want to know it all? Think carefully before you answer because you won't like what you hear.'

'I want to hear it.' She didn't hesitate, and his smile was cynical as he slowly shook his head.

'The arrogance of youth...' He shook his head again as he said, 'I was young once, Jessica, young and crazily in love. And crazy is the right word for the feeling that filled me at that time; it wasn't rational or logical.'

She waited quietly, calling on all the fortitude she had to prevent the pain from showing. She'd asked for this, she told herself, demanded it. But she hadn't dreamt it would hurt so much.

'Netta was beautiful in a wild, gypsy sort of way, with long black hair down to her waist, and eyes...eyes very much like yours,' he said softly. 'But whereas yours are clear and warm and velvety soft hers were fiery brown; they almost glowed at times with her intensity of spirit. We met at university and lived together for the last year. Once we'd qualified we both decided London was the place to be. I asked her to marry me but she wanted more time. I could understand that...'

He paused, his eyes looking inwards with an expression that frightened her. 'She'd had a rough time at home, apparently, with an alcoholic father and a mother who took in "lodgers"—male lodgers to pay the bills, who stayed one night and were gone in the morning. So I could see marriage wasn't something that held much attraction. She'd qualified with a first and got an excellent job in a laboratory; I began a spot of wheeling and dealing and found I'd got a flair for it, so things were looking rosy. We argued a lot but part of what I loved about her was her strength, so...'

The rain had become a steady downpour now, drumming on the roof of the car and running in rivulets down the windscreen, but they were both oblivious to the storm outside.

'We got a flat together but being on our own, away from the craziness of university life, things began to go wrong. Netta had these rages—that's the only way I can explain it—black, malignant rages that the slightest thing could set off. Oh, she was always prettily penitent afterwards, using all the wiles at her disposal—which were plenty.

'My sister came to stay for a few weeks and things were better for a while, and then one day Netta didn't come home from work...'

'An accident?' Jessica asked faintly, thinking of the few facts she knew.

'Nothing so noble.' He looked at her, his eyes deep pools of dark torment, but nothing could have prepared her for his next words. 'At one in the morning, when I was frantic, there was a phone call. It was Netta, and she was at some address I'd never heard of. She was crying and I couldn't get any sense out of her beyond the fact that she wanted me to go round there and collect her. Becky insisted she come with me—neither of us had been to sleep, worrying about Netta—and I drove to this address in a sleazy part of the city and picked her up. She'd had a back-street abortion.'

'*Colt!*' She stared at him, unable to take it in.

'She was at the flat of a woman she worked with who'd arranged the abortion for her, but things hadn't quite gone according to plan and Netta was feeling worse than she'd expected. Neither of them would give me the name and address of the butcher; I think they were both frightened of what I'd do. They were right to be frightened,' he finished grimly.

'What did you do?' she asked shakily.

'What could I do? Packed her in the car with Becky and drove home. We had a row to end all rows. I couldn't believe she'd killed our child, a child created in love—or so I thought.'

'It was your baby?' Jessica asked bewilderedly. 'But then why the abortion?'

'She didn't want children, ties, anything that would put limits on her,' he said bitterly. 'Her career was just beginning to take off and that was all she was concerned with. She'd thought she could get away with it without telling me but then, when things didn't go according to plan, she panicked; otherwise…otherwise I'd never have known part of me was killed. I knew if I stayed there with her I'd kill her, I was so angry, so desperate…' He ran his hand over his face, pushing at his skin. 'So I left her with Becky and walked to a friend's house. He listened and then we opened a bottle of whisky.'

'Colt, I'm so sorry.' She hadn't expected this, never in her wildest dreams, but then they said truth was stranger than fiction…

'Oh, there's more, Jessica. The best is yet to come, as they say.' She couldn't put a name to the dark emotion in his voice; she just knew she never wanted to hear such agony of soul again. 'Netta phoned about six in the morning; she was haemorrhaging and needed medical attention. She was hysterical—' He paused, his voice thick and uneven. 'There was no remorse for what she'd done, not the slightest regret about the baby. She was just scared and angry she'd been caught out.

'I told her I couldn't drive her, I'd been drinking, but I'd call her an ambulance and meet her at the hospital. She slammed the phone down on me—and half an hour later she was dead. And she took Becky with her.' His bitterness was tangible, with the energy of a live thing, snaking round the car in a wave of dark, virulent hatred that caused Jessica to clutch her throat as her breath constricted.

'I don't know exactly what happened; I never will. But I think Netta persuaded Becky to cancel the ambulance and drive her to the hospital, knowing how mad it'd make me. Becky was only learning to drive and hadn't much confidence; she wouldn't have attempted such a thing without coercion. It would have taken no more than four or five minutes for an ambulance to get there—*four or five minutes*, damn her. She'd obviously waited longer than that for Becky to get ready, as the head-on collision that killed them happened just a couple of streets away a good thirty minutes later.'

He looked at her with tortured eyes, taking in her white face and trembling lips, the dark velvet of her gaze soft with compassion. 'I blamed myself at first, for both their deaths. I'd driven Netta to do what she did and it'd killed her and Becky. But then, on the day of the funeral, I met Netta's parents.'

There was a bewildered note in his voice now, a deep, bitter perplexity that caught at her heartstrings. 'They were perfectly normal people, Jessica—it'd all been lies. Her father was a bank manager and her mother a teacher. Netta had left home at sixteen, telling them they were boring. From the little they said, she'd made their life hell for years before moving in with some other students while she worked for her A levels and sleeping with anything in trousers.

'The things I found out…'

He straightened, his voice hardening. 'My mother had a stroke the evening of Becky's funeral and died a few weeks later. The doctor said she'd given up the will to live. I could understand that. For a time after their deaths the same thing happened to me, and then…then I fought back,' he said grimly.

Jessica shivered, although it wasn't the coolness of the air that had sent a feathery chill down her spine. She should have known there was more to Colt's isolation than her supposition that he couldn't forgive his sister for his fiancée's death, or mourning for a lost love. He was too big a man, in every sense of the word, for pettiness or bigotry. If it had been as she had suspected he would have mourned them both, but then got on with the rest of his life without blaming Becky for an accident. But she had known really, right at the bottom of her. All along she had sensed there was much more to Colt Irons than the bare facts revealed.

'One woman, a woman I had thought I knew, and loved and trusted, a woman who turned out to be merely a figment of my imagination, managed to kill three people, two of whom were more dear to me than my own life. I grieved for the baby, but not in the same way as for Becky and my mother. My father had entrusted them to me when he died and I'd promised to take care of them both. I'd betrayed both him and myself.'

'But it wasn't your fault,' Jessica protested quickly. 'You couldn't have known—'

'*I should have known.*' She flinched at his hardness and his voice was quieter as he said, 'I should have known, Jessica. I let a pretty face and an agile, experienced body fool me into believing Netta was what I wanted her to be, and others paid the ultimate price for my mistake.'

'Everyone makes mistakes.' She reached out and touched his arm but his muscles were like granite under her fingers, hard and unresponsive.

'I don't; not any more. I made up my mind I would succeed; for my parents and my sister I would succeed and make something of the Irons name, build a legacy from the ashes. But love...' His eyes fixed on her now and she saw they were unblinking. 'Love and happiness have no place in the equation. I don't deserve them.'

'You don't deserve them?' She stared at him, aghast. 'Of course you deserve happiness, Colt; everyone does. You don't think for a moment your parents or Becky would want you to be miserable, do you? The fault was Netta's, you know that; you weren't to blame for believing in her, loving her.

'Look at me with William and Jo—I had no idea they were seeing each other, sleeping together; they fooled me utterly. But I do know that if they hadn't betrayed me I would have married William believing I was doing the right thing, and it would have been the biggest mistake of my life because I didn't love him. I thought I did, but now I know it was a shadow of the real thing.'

She saw him blink a second before a shutter blanked the slate-grey eyes.

'Human beings make mistakes, Colt. It's scary but it's real life,' she said gently, her heart aching with his grief and pain.

'And the casualties, the innocents who get hurt?' he asked harshly. 'You're telling me that's just part of the whole great, wonderful scenario?'

'It's not wonderful but it happens,' she said steadily.

'Not if I can help it,' he said tightly. 'I run my life the way I want to now, Jessica. No flowery words, no messy emotion, just plain, unvarnished fact. I know where I stand and the women know where they stand; there's no chance for mistakes. You say you set some store by the truth—well, that's it.'

She wasn't reaching him. She stared at him, at his cold, harsh face that was so handsome and so dear. If he wasn't so handsome? Wasn't wealthy and powerful and influential? Would she have had more of a chance with him then? she asked herself painfully. She'd never know, would she? She had to deal with it as it was, here and now. All the preconceived ideas she'd had about him had been swept away in the last few minutes, his revelations about his past life burning up all her feelings of self-protection and self-preservation. Somehow what she felt wasn't so important any more.

'Yes, I do set great store by the truth now,' she said slowly, choosing her words carefully. 'The affair with William taught me that honesty between a man and a woman is absolutely essential. I love you, Colt; that's the *truth*. I've loved you for some time, but I was frightened to let you know.'

'No.' The word was grating. 'What you term as love is physical desire. We strike sparks off each other, that's all, Jessica.'

'It is not.' She took a deep breath but her voice didn't falter. 'That might be an ingredient of my feeling for you but it's only a part. I know what I feel, and it's love.'

'Jessica, you're a romantic, a visionary,' he said heavily, his hard face broodingly dark. 'You imagined you loved William, and when you were let down so badly it left you wide open for whatever followed.'

'You mean you,' she said flatly.

'Me.' The word was final and so was his expression as he turned the key in the ignition and the car growled into life. 'I've done a lot of things in my life I'm not too proud of, but taking advantage of a woman is not one of them. I want you, you know that, but you've convinced yourself I mean more to you than could ever be possible. There's no future with me, there never was, and one day you'll see it clearly.'

The heavens opened on the drive home, the torrent of rain loud and blindingly fierce, causing the windscreen wipers to labour and the car to crawl along at a quarter of its normal speed. As they approached London the storm began to ease, but the night was overcast and dark, with a chill in the air that was more reminiscent of November than late summer. The whole setting was so in tune with her thoughts that it would have been funny if it weren't so tragic, Jessica thought desperately, like some well-staged play or film that could be controlled at the director's whim. But this was no play—this was real life. She was losing the man she loved and there wasn't a thing she could do about it.

She was vitally aware of the big body so close to hers, the tension that was in every line of his muscled frame reflected in her own. There was no pretence of lazy control now, no cool mockery or indolent remoteness. He had bared his soul and she could feel his anger at himself for doing so, for allowing those few minutes of vulnerability. She searched his closed features from under the shelter of her eyelashes, her gaze moving over the grim tightness of his mouth, the hard, masculine planes of his cheekbones, but the cold profile could have been cast in stone for all it revealed.

When they drew up outside her house the quiet street was shrouded in a thick grey mist that enfolded the car in a world of its own, blurring the view beyond the windows into a dark void. He had said little on the journey, responding to her occasional forlorn attempts at conversation with curt monosyllables that left her in no doubt as to how he felt. He wanted to be rid of her, as quickly as possible and without any further embarrassing and difficult disclosures, she thought painfully. But the thought that this was goodbye, that she was going to have to spend the rest of her life without him, was filling her with a mixture of desperation and fear. He had turned her world upside down, set every standard she had for herself on its end, and now he was just going to drive away? It wasn't fair; none of this was fair.

'Thank you for driving me down to Brindale,' she said quietly as he cut the engine, leaning back in his seat without looking at her. 'You wouldn't really have gone down to see Harry, would you?'

'Jessica…' He stopped, his voice hard and clipped as he answered tersely, 'No, I wouldn't.'

'You drove me down because you knew how upset I'd be about Carol,' she stated flatly.

He said nothing; it hadn't been a question. But as she prompted, 'Didn't you?' he swore softly, an explicit oath that carried pain and frustration at its core.

'Goodnight, Jessica.' His body was rigid, his voice taut, but she knew she wouldn't get a second chance at this. She had to break through, find the tiniest chink in the armour, and then perhaps there would be a hope that she could at least remain on the perimeter of his life and keep chipping away at that shield that the years had cemented in place.

She leant over, reaching up and kissing the side of his mouth in a small, tentative kiss that quivered at his lack of response. How did you go about seducing a man who was possessed of a terrifying sexual magnetism that experience and nature had rendered irresistible? she asked herself helplessly. A man who was well versed in the arts of lovemaking, who was compelling, fascinating, and as cold as ice when he wanted to be—like now.

'Colt?' She was stretched up against him, her breath fanning his mouth and one hand stroking his broad neck, her fingers moving up into the crisp black hair. She felt him shudder at her touch and that alone gave her the courage to continue as he still didn't say a word, remaining perfectly still. 'Colt, kiss me, please.'

'Whatever game you're playing it had better stop right now.' He turned his head as he spoke, intending to look into her eyes, but in the same instant she swooped on his mouth, her lips warm and half-open as she took the initiative for the first time in their acquaintance.

He froze, for one long, heart-stopping moment when her blood pounded in her ears with such force she thought she would faint, and then his arms went round her as he groaned deep in his throat, the sound more animal than human. His hands moved to her head, cupping her face with his long fingers as his mouth feverishly took hers in a predatory kiss that ravished the soft contours almost savagely, his breathing frenzied.

He wanted her, *he did*; he wanted her... The dark delight of knowing that he hadn't been able to resist, that his desire had outweighed that intimidating will of steel, increased the tumult of wild pleasure that was coursing through her veins.

She loved him; she had to show him that she loved and wanted and needed him; self-preservation had no place in her emotions now. She would take whatever he was prepared to give—a week, a month, a year. But she would hope for more, hope that she could penetrate that outer shell and begin to mean something more to him than just a young and desirable body. He cared for her; as a person he cared for her—his actions, not his words, had proved that. So that was a start, wasn't it? Love might come later, even to Colt Irons...

Her fingers were still threaded in the strong, springy blackness of his hair as she held him close, and as he drank from her mouth, the kiss so erotic that she moaned with the pleasure of it, she felt she was drowning in the passion he induced so magically.

His hands had slipped beneath the bottom of her blouse, cupping the swell of her full breasts as his thumbs caressed the rosy peaks until she thought she would die with what his hands and mouth were doing to her. And then, as a long shudder racked his frame, he stopped. 'This is madness,' he ground out through clenched teeth as he forcibly pushed her away. 'Sheer madness.'

'Why?' She was panting softly, her voice exhilarated. 'Why is it? You want me and I want you; you've said it often enough.'

'You know why, Jessica. You'll get hurt and I don't want that,' he said tightly. 'You're not ready to handle this.'

'You said the others didn't get hurt, that they could handle it.'

'*You aren't like the others.*' The air went still, the world stopped spinning, all nature held its breath.

'Colt—'

'Damn you, Jessica.' His voice was quiet now, quiet and flat. 'I don't want this.' He was out of the car before she could stop him, walking round the bonnet without glancing at her, and opening her door with a violent jerk that betrayed his agitation.

She slid out slowly, her mind racing and her heart thudding so loud she was sure he must be able to hear it. If she didn't do something now, stop him from leaving like this, she would lose him for good. How could he do this? After the months of chasing her, how could he not give her a chance? He wasn't human...

'Goodbye, Jessica,' he said quietly, standing back a

pace as she stood up with her back to the car. The two words were ominously final, and with them something in her snapped and the words flowed hot and fierce.

'And that's it? "Goodbye, Jessica"?' she hissed angrily, almost spitting the words into his cold face. 'You've decided it's goodbye and that's it? What gives you the right to act like this, Colt Irons? And don't give me the excuse that you're doing it for me, to save me pain, because I don't believe you. You're scared—scared stiff of taking a chance on love and life. There are thousands, *millions* of people out there who get hurt, and hurt badly; you aren't the only one to find out you've made a fool of yourself. How do you think I felt when I arrived at that church and waited and waited?' she asked furiously.

'That's enough.' His voice was icy, his face dark and furious as he glared down into her blazing eyes.

'You can't shut yourself away for ever,' she said, totally ignoring his warning. 'And however full your little black book is that's exactly what you've been doing. You've only given your body, like a robot, an animal—'

'I mean it, Jessica.' He turned and walked round to the driver's side but her words followed him, shooting across the air with deadly accuracy.

'You've told yourself that you owe it to your parents and Becky to be miserable; is that it?' she continued relentlessly. 'You're paying the price still, for something that was never your debt anyway. But that isn't all of it, is it? If you open yourself up, take a chance, you become like the rest of us—vulnerable. That's what you really can't take.'

His eyes were lethal as he glanced at her for one moment before sliding his big body into the car, but she lowered her head and spoke through the open passenger door. 'I was devastated when William jilted me. And when I found out about Jo I thought my world had come to an end. But it hadn't. I hadn't slept with William, I know, but my commitment was absolute and I felt hurt and humiliated and less than nothing. And then I met you, at the fête and then that party, and you told me to start living again, to come back into the real world. How could you bring me back into the land of the living only to leave me in a worse state than I was in before?'

'I never promised you anything—'

'*I love you.*' The words were a low moan and, like before, the world went silent as they faced each other through the car. 'I'm prepared to take a chance, even with you telling me you are as you are. I…I haven't slept with anyone before but I want to sleep with you. I want memories, if nothing else.'

Her voice broke as the tears began to wash down her cheeks but still he didn't move, his eyes naked and anguished and rent with a hundred personal demons as they devoured her face. And just when she thought she had got through, that he was going to reach across the space dividing them, his hand moved and the powerful engine growled into life.

'Colt, please, please don't go. You can't leave—'

Even as she spoke he leant across and shut the passenger door, the car leaping away in the next moment as the engine screamed in a fury of noise and the tyres sent loose pieces of gravel spinning into the air.

She watched him go without moving at all, her eyes wide and disbelieving and her senses numbed by all that had gone before. She had said it all; she couldn't have done more. She had bared her soul, as had he, but it hadn't been enough. In the final analysis it hadn't been enough. He had left her.

After a few minutes the thin drizzle permeated her summer jacket and began to drip cold droplets down her neck, but still she didn't move, her legs anchored to the greasy, grimy pavement by the abject misery that had her in its grip.

She would never be happy again, never know the carefree pleasure, the sheer joy of being alive that had punctuated her first twenty-four years. Evermore, whatever she was doing, whoever she was with, the spectre of a tall, dark man with stormy grey eyes and a mouth that promised heaven would be at her shoulder. And it was worse now, now that she knew the real Colt whom he had revealed so reluctantly that day. His pain was her pain, his anguish lacerated her heart with the intensity of a flaming spear, in spite of his cruel rejection. She wanted to hate him; she had every reason to hate him, she told herself bitterly. But she couldn't. She loved him; she would always love him…

It was a full ten minutes before she went into the house and by that time she was desolate. Half of her had, if not exactly expected, then desperately hoped that he would come back before it was too late.

But he hadn't—he wouldn't, she acknowledged bleakly, pulling off her damp clothes and donning her bathrobe before walking along to the bathroom and spending almost an hour soaking in a hot tub. But despite the sojourn in the steamy water she was still chilled to the marrow when she snuggled down into bed later, the rawness coming from within and not without.

She couldn't sleep for a long time, her mind replaying the events of the last twenty-four hours over and over in a torturous and self-destructive series of résumés that had her drinking hot chocolate at three a.m., still without having shut her eyes. Should she have acted differently? *Could* she? she asked herself as she sat cross-legged on the bed with her hands cupped round the mug of milky chocolate. She wrinkled her brow as the rich, aromatic fragrance teased her nostrils.

No. The answer was unequivocal. Sooner or later she would have revealed her feelings for him, because she knew now that he wouldn't have given up the chase until then. He had expected a light affair, a brief flirtation, and it was only when she had told him how she really felt about him that the pursuit had stopped, the hunter becoming the hunted.

Strangely, in spite of the grinding pain and heartache,

the knowledge that she couldn't have acted differently allowed her to finish the chocolate and lie down in bed again with a clearer mind. And almost immediately she fell into a deep, dreamless sleep in which there were no yesterdays, no tomorrows, and no present, with its searing hopelessness.

CHAPTER TEN

JESSICA awoke the next morning a few minutes before her small alarm clock gave its strident call at seven, her mind vitally alert and every nerve and sinew painfully aware that this was the first day of the rest of her life without Colt. In spite of the lack of sleep and exhausting emotion of the day and evening before, she felt wide awake and positively hyperactive, her senses jangling and over-sensitised.

Russell was inordinately glad to see her in the office that morning, and of the two of them Jessica had to admit he looked the worse for wear. 'The baby's just not sleeping,' he informed her wearily as he sat gazing at the mountain of work on his desk with a marked lack of enthusiasm. 'He was fine in the hospital, but now he's home he's crying all the time. We didn't shut our eyes all night.'

'Oh, dear.' She wanted to be sympathetic, she really did, but somehow Russell's problems didn't seem to be on a par with hers. 'I'm sure he'll settle down over the next twenty-four hours, Russell, when the feeds get sorted and everything. How's Monica?' she asked carefully.

'Irritable and weepy,' he said gloomily. 'The midwife came just as I left this morning and Monica dissolved on her before she got through the door.' He sighed heavily, his eyes tragic.

'It'll all work out, you'll see.' She glanced at his loaded desk. 'Why don't you give me some of your more urgent stuff and put your feet up for an hour or so? I'm not doing anything tonight, so I don't mind staying late and clearing some more then.' She needed the work, she told herself silently—anything to stop herself thinking. The short journey to work had been torture when her mind hadn't been occupied, Colt's face in front of her every inch of the way.

'You're an angel.' Russell gave her the sort of brave, weak smile people gave when they felt sorry for themselves. 'An absolute angel. I don't deserve you, Jess.'

'I know,' she said wryly, forcing a smile to soften her words.

She got through the day and the mountain of work somehow, leaving the silent office block at just after nine, utterly exhausted and ready to drop. Once back at the bedsit a meal seemed too much of a bother, but she forced herself to eat a sandwich and drink a glass of milk before falling into bed, her limbs as heavy as lead and her head pounding.

She slept deeply for a couple of hours and then woke with a start, conscious that she had been dreaming of Colt but unable to remember exactly what beyond a vague impression of doom and gloom. From that point on she cat-napped, waking finally at just before six and running herself a long, hot bath to soak away the aches and pains of a restless night.

That scenario seemed to set a pattern for the next few days: work and more work at the office, until she arrived home late and exhausted to a night of tossing and turning and dark, nightmarish dreams dominated by a tall, dark man with steel-grey eyes and a cold, handsome face.

Nevertheless, when Russell rang her at home on Saturday morning at just after nine she had already been up for a couple of hours and was beginning to spring-clean the bedsit, driven on by something outside of herself in spite of her exhaustion.

'Jess?' Russell was using the slightly mournful 'life must go on at all costs' voice he had used all week, which had grown a little hard to take after four days. 'We had another bad night last night.'

'Did you?' Join the club, she thought militantly.

'Look, I'm ringing to ask you a big favour. I wouldn't bother you normally, but it's just that this is particularly important. I know you've worked your socks off this week...'

'Russell,' she said patiently, 'get on with it.'

'It's just that Monica and I were going to a reception tonight which could be useful to me business-wise. The invitation stems from that project I did for Cantaena's last year, remember? Old man Cantaena was well pleased with the results and he's holding a party at the Dawford tonight. Everyone will be there...' There was a pause and then, 'The thing is, Monica just isn't up to it and I wondered if you'd partner me?' he asked hopefully.

No way. No way could she endure a high-powered social occasion of the sort that this one would be, Jessica thought desperately as her mind raced for a plausible excuse. 'I'm sorry, Russell, but I can't make it tonight,' she said quickly.

'Jess, please. It isn't the sort of thing I can arrive at without a partner, and you know more about the business than I do in some areas. I'm not intending to stay late, not after the week I've had...' There was a poignant pause followed by a despairing sigh, and although the cajolery was blatant Jessica felt a stab of guilt. 'I'll make it worth your while,' he added in a wheedling tone. 'A few days off or a bonus—whichever you'd prefer. Did you have something special planned for this evening?'

'Not exactly,' she admitted quietly. A phone call to Carol, who was due home from the hospital that afternoon, followed by an early night could hardly be termed special. Two minutes later, when she replaced the receiver, it was with the knowledge that she had been foolish enough to commit herself to an evening of purgatory, a fact that remained burning in her head for the rest of the day and later that evening as she got ready for the night ahead.

The fine coffee-coloured silk of the outfit she'd bought what seemed a lifetime ago for the evening out with Colt was a painful, vibrant reminder of all she had lost, but it was also the only suitable item in her wardrobe for the sort of occasion Russell had described.

A week. Had it only been a week since she discovered she loved Colt? she asked herself disbelievingly as she stroked a soft shade of gold eyeshadow on her lids, followed by a touch of mascara to her long, thick lashes. How could you find someone and lose them in a week? She hoped this feeling deep inside her would get better in time, but as yet the gnawing agony was so severe it stopped her breath at times.

She looked at her white face, the eyes dark pools of anguish, and hastily applied a little blusher to her pale skin. From what she had seen of Señor Cantaena the year before, he wasn't the sort of man to appreciate someone arriving at his party looking as though they were going to their execution.

The red carpet was out at the five-star hotel deep in the heart of London when she emerged from the taxi an hour later, Russell at her side. They were ushered through the wildly luxurious reception area and into a massive ballroom that was all velvet drapes and sparkling chandeliers, and which blended perfectly with the exclusive creations and glittering diamonds of the people within.

'Wow.' Even Russell was impressed. 'Do you think anyone else in this room was changing a dirty nappy half an hour ago?' he asked in a wry undertone that brought a reluctant smile to Jessica's face.

'I doubt it.' She took a deep breath, widening the smile and forcing her body language to speak confidence. First impressions were all-important at this kind of 'see and be seen' social affair; businesses were made or broken on less.

It was as she glanced casually round the room, her head held proudly upright and her carriage erect, that a pair of slate-grey eyes pierced her to the spot. 'Colt...'

She must have spoken his name out loud because Russell turned to her, his gaze following hers.

'So it is.' Russell's voice was speculative. 'And who's the beauty at his side, I wonder? I'll say one thing for him—he certainly can pick 'em.'

Jessica hadn't noticed Colt's companion; her thunderous heartbeat and swirling head had made anything but that cold, handsome face fade into oblivion, but now she saw someone was pressed close to him, her arm through his, and, as Russell had remarked, the woman was beautiful. Beautiful and elegant and quite, quite stunning from the top of her dark, sophisticated head to her expensively shod feet, her voluptuous figure clothed in a daringly cut gown of ivory satin and her throat and ears dripping in jewels.

Jessica wanted to go home—oh, she did want to go home... She was aware of the little whimper in her mind even as she tore her eyes from Colt's and inclined her head towards Russell, her smile brittle. 'Well, into the fray. Lead on, Macduff.' It was amazing how normal you could sound when you were breaking apart inside, she thought remotely as they walked further into the room, accepting a glass of champagne from one of the waiters who populated the vast expanse of floor. She was bleeding, slowly and painfully, and no one knew.

'Jessica, Russell...'

She had been hoping against hope that he would have the good taste to avoid her, but as the deep, husky voice sounded just behind her she acknowledged that she'd known he would come over. She turned slowly, expelling a long, silent breath she hadn't been aware she was holding, and looked up into his face. He looked magnificent, the dark evening suit accentuating the broad, muscled shoulders and big chest and, strangely, giving him more of a predatory air than ever.

'Good evening, Colt.' She heard Russell speak just at the side of her, but if her life had depended on it she couldn't have said anything at that moment so she merely smiled, inclining her head first at Colt and then at his consort, whose eyes were tight on her face. There was something in the other woman's gaze that was calculating and cold, the sapphire-blue eyes dissecting her make-up and hair and pricing her clothes to the last penny. But rather than finding it intimidating Jessica found reality was taking on the feeling of a play, a bad, third-rate drama.

'How do you do?' It wasn't play-acting that made her voice cool and contained—her mind and senses seemed to have gone into deep freeze, allowing an unnatural calm to take over. And, although she didn't understand it, she was grateful for the lack of feeling that enabled her to face the pair of them with a dignity that was unmistakable.

His companion was even more beautiful close up, her smooth, creamy skin without a flaw and her eyes a brilliant blue that resembled polished glass—but she had no warmth about her, no softness. Jessica heard Colt make the necessary introductions and she must have responded in some form, because the conversation took the route of normal social chit-chat, everyone smiling and so decorous.

It was as Russell was answering Colt's enquiry after Monica that the sapphire-blue eyes homed in, fine eyebrows raised in a little questioning frown. 'Oh, you *work* for him…' It was said with delicate disdain. 'I thought you were his girlfriend.'

'No.' Jessica managed a smile in spite of the intended snub. 'I'm Russell's personal assistant.'

'Really…?' Both the tone and the lack of interest in the drawled-out word indicated that the beautiful brunette had decided Jessica was not worth cultivating, her social status being so low down the scale as to render her unimportant. And it was in that moment that a dart of something hot pierced the ice.

How dared he? How dared he subject her to this? There was no logic in her rage, no objectivity, just a dark, violent flood of emotion that was as unwelcome as it was dangerous, and she lowered her head as the men continued to talk, blinking quickly to dispel the red mist before her eyes. She mustn't let it get to her—she mustn't.

She was aware of Russell extolling the joys of fatherhood, but she heard his voice from a long way off. By then the thaw had well and truly set in. She found she was battling with feelings she had never experienced before, their fierceness devastating. Certainly the pain and confusion she had felt when William had betrayed her had been merely lukewarm compared to this violent, consuming rawness.

'Jessica?' Russell nudged her and she came back from a distance to find they were all looking at her. 'I said we'd be pleased to do more work for Colt in the future.' It was a statement that merely needed her polite acquiescence, but she found she couldn't do it—not with that woman's arm tucked in his, and the length of her body against his thigh.

She had been honest with him, she had been prepared to forget all her principles, all her ideals, all the things that made her who she was. She had offered herself unreservedly and he had thrown it back in her face. Well, fine—*fine*—but she was blowed if he was going to rub her nose in it too. If this meant the end of her career, the loss of her credibility, then that was fine too, but no power on earth would stop her telling Colt Irons exactly what he could do with more work.

'I'm sorry, Russell.' And she was—she was sorry for Russell, who was about to have a mini grenade explode in his smiling face. 'But I wouldn't work for Colt if he was the last man on earth.'

'*Jessica!*' Russell stared at her and then turned to Colt, his arms outstretched like a penitent seeking absolution. 'She didn't mean it, Colt—'

'I think she did.' There was a brilliant darkness glittering deep in the slate-grey eyes, but apart from that show of emotion Colt's face could have been etched in stone.

'Well, really! I've never heard such insolence—'

'Colt, she's tired—she's been working too hard this week; it's my fault.' Russell cut into the brunette's outraged words desperately as he saw his wonderful evening turning to ashes in front of him. 'Jessica, tell him...'

'Tell him what?' She met the grey eyes with a kamikaze defiance that felt wonderfully good considering she was destroying both her career and that last faint hope she had nourished in her heart that he would open up just the merest crack and let her in. 'Tell him that he's an arrogant, cruel, stupid fool of a man? Is that what you want me to say, Russell? The truth?'

She saw the words register in Colt's eyes like tiny blows, but she was past feeling anything now, the self-destruct button well and truly pressed. 'There's an old saying, Colt, that pigeons always come home to roost—which, roughly translated, means we get what we deserve. Well, that's what you deserve.' She gestured at the incensed brunette whose scandalised face was a picture.

'You—!' As the brunette went to strike, Colt's hand fastened on her wrist like a steel band but his eyes didn't waver from Jessica's face, penetrating her heart and her mind like a laser.

She had been on the edge of hysteria, she realised that now, but his complete lack of emotion was like a douche of cold water on the flames of bitter hurt and anguish. She stood, shaking slightly, amazed to find that the party was going on all around them, people completely unaware of the little scene being enacted in their midst.

'Are you going to let some little secretary talk to you like that?' The brunette's voice was savage. 'And insult me?'

'Insult you, Veronica?' Colt's voice was soft and flat. 'As far as I understand Jessica said I deserve you—you consider that an insult?' He was about to say more, turning to Jessica and Russell as Veronica flounced away, when Señor Cantaena joined them, his greeting to Colt effusive.

As Russell edged closer to the two men Jessica seized the opportunity to melt into the background, the trembling that was affecting her limbs making her feel physically sick. What had she done? What *had* she done? As she made her way to the ladies' cloakroom, her head buzzing, she couldn't believe she had acted in such a way.

Mercifully the cloakroom was empty. After sinking down onto a quilted chair for a few moments she forced herself to stand and splash cold water over her wrists, before holding her hands to her burning cheeks as she surveyed her flushed reflection in the ornate mirror. 'Jessica, Jessica...' she whispered brokenly. 'You've really done it this time.' The mouth moved, the eyes flickered, but she could hardly believe the girl staring back at her was her own self.

She felt she didn't know herself any more, that she was a stranger placed into a familiar skin and one who was out of control. And it was his fault. 'It is,' she said more loudly. She had been an ordinary, nice girl until she met him—certainly not this fire-and-brimstone creature that emerged every time she was within a few yards of Colt Irons.

He brought feelings to the surface she hadn't imagined she was capable of feeling, and not just those of rage either. She remembered some of the more erotic dreams that had plagued her since she had first set eyes on that big, dark, muscled figure and her cheeks burnt hotter. What had he done to her? What was he still continuing to do to her? If this was love then it certainly wasn't the enjoyable, comfortable emotion she had always imagined it to be.

She couldn't go back in there. She had never run away from anything or anyone in her life, but she just couldn't

go back into that room; she didn't trust herself to. If Colt
hadn't defused the situation she would have made a big-
ger fool of herself than she had managed; she knew that
now. And if Veronica came anywhere near her, with her
smooth insolence and contemptuous eyes, blood would
flow. 'Some little secretary.' Jessica ground her teeth
angrily.

'Oh, Jessica…' The sigh of despair that followed was
very real. William wouldn't recognise the gentle, quiet
girl he had known, she thought painfully. Perhaps she
was more like Jo than she wanted to believe.

She wrote a short note to Russell apologising for her
behaviour, which she didn't expect him to understand or
condone, and after checking that the coast was clear gave
it to one of the waiters before leaving the hotel quietly
and quickly. She wasn't running away—she wasn't, she
told herself as she stepped into the summer night. She
was just saving everyone from further embarrassment.
The excuse rang hollow even to her own ears.

Outside it was pleasantly warm and still light, the evening mellow and still, and on an impulse she couldn't
explain to herself she gave the taxi driver her mother's
address rather than her own. The fifteen-mile journey
seemed to pass in as many seconds as she sat huddled
in the back of the taxi, her head spinning with a thousand
images and her stomach churning as she relived the awful scene with Colt.

Her mother was tending her tiny garden when Jessica
let herself in with her key, after receiving no reply to
her knock, the two fat tabby cats who shared her mother's life and tended to rule the roost sitting in idle con-
templation on the small wooden seat in the neat terraced
garden. Jessica stood for a moment in the kitchen doorway, silently surveying her mother while she worked.

She looked tired and older somehow, Jessica thought
suddenly—two words she didn't normally associate with
her busy mother—and it came to her that the affair with

Jo and herself had affected her mother more than she had thought.

'Jessica?' Her mother glanced up from the weeding of a group of yellow and mauve pansies, and her face broke into a welcome smile at the sight of her daughter. 'Hello, darling, what a lovely surprise.'

It was the genuine pleasure in her mother's face that caused the floodgates to open. She hadn't intended to burden her mother with her problems, but as the tears exploded from Jessica's eyes, nose and mouth Mrs Taylor hurried to her side, her voice anxious as she said, 'Darling, oh, darling, whatever's wrong?'

It was some time before Jessica could control herself sufficiently to talk, and by then they were sitting on the little bench under a silver birch tree, the cats having been brushed off—much to their chagrin.

She told her mother everything in the quiet of the summer evening—from the first moment at the fête when Colt had come into her life, right up to the disastrous finale that night when she had disgraced herself so utterly. 'Everything is such a mess—' she raised swollen eyes to her mother's concerned face '—and I can't see any way out. I would give anything not to love him, but I do. I just can't help it.'

'I know, I know.' Her mother held her close for precious minutes and Jessica relaxed against her, something she couldn't remember doing for a long, long time. 'I've told you before, my darling, you are too much like me for your own good. We are the type of women who love once, Jessica, just once.'

'But that's all right if the person you love loves you back.' Jessica sniffed forlornly. 'But he doesn't. In fact right at this moment he probably hates me for causing such a scene. He's always so in control, so aloof; that sort of incident was everything he dislikes,' she said on a little sob, rubbing her wet nose with the back of her hand as though she were four instead of twenty-four.

'Here.' Her mother handed her a lavender-scented

handkerchief, bringing back distant memories of bygone days when Jessica had run to her with bloody knees or cut fingers and her mother had dried her tears.

'Now, first things first,' Mrs Taylor said briskly when Jessica had mopped up. 'He clearly doesn't hate you—in fact I'd say just the opposite—but whether his love for you is enough to banish all the baggage from the past I really don't know.'

'He doesn't love me.' Jessica raised tragic eyes to her mother's face. 'At this minute in time he probably wants to strangle me.'

'Well, be that as it may, you love him,' her mother stated firmly. 'And I really can't see that the man you've described would be such a fool as to throw away your love when he's had time to think about it.'

'Oh, Mum, you should have seen the woman who was with him tonight,' Jessica said miserably. 'He can have his pick of the most beautiful women around. Why should he bother with me, anyway? And he's had five days to think about it,' she added flatly.

'Darling, we're talking about barriers that have been in place for most of his adult life,' her mother said gently. 'Barriers that life and hard experience have made even more rigid through the years. You have to give him time and be patient.'

'You don't know him.' Jessica sighed heavily, her face pale and shadowed in the dusky light. 'You just don't know how his mind works.'

'I know you,' her mother said softly. 'And believe me, Jessica, one thing life and hard experience does is make you recognise the jewel amongst a pile of ordinary stones. Like I said, I don't think the man you've told me about tonight is a fool, and he'll know a jewel when he finds one. Be patient; if you love him, be patient. Learn from my mistakes. I left your father because I felt I couldn't live with him, but living without him has been harder.'

'Oh, Mum.' Jessica clasped her mother's hands in her

own. 'I'm sorry. Really. I never understood until recently how you felt; you'd never said.'

'I know; stiff upper lip and all that,' her mother said quietly. 'What fools we can be at times, Jessica. Darling, I don't know if this is the right time, or whether it will help or hinder, but...but how would you feel about your father and I getting together again?'

'Mum!' Jessica stared at her in absolute amazement. 'You mean...? When? What's been happening?'

'Oh, I suppose it was all the awful pain and confusion over Jo running off with William that prompted me to really talk to him again,' the older woman said softly. 'You are both his daughters too, and I felt he was the only person who could understand.

'I don't understand Jo, Jessica; I don't think I even like her. But she is my daughter, and I love her. I know that doesn't make sense but that's how it is. At that time I felt I'd lost you completely. I knew you blamed me partly for the whole sorry mess, and I broke down on the phone to your father one evening. The next morning he was knocking on my door.'

'He was?' Jessica was astounded. 'I didn't know he'd been back in England.'

'He only stayed for a few hours,' her mother said softly. 'But it was long enough to get some things sorted out. He's retiring at the end of the year—he's had enough now—and...and he asked me to marry him when he comes home.'

'And you're going to?' Jessica asked weakly, unable to take in what she was hearing. In the early days of the separation, before the divorce and for some time after, she had prayed for just this very thing night after night after night, pleading with God, promising anything if only her parents could be reunited.

Her mother nodded slowly. 'I love him, Jessica. I've never loved anyone else and I never will,' she said simply. 'I'm not blind to his faults—he's selfish and a perfectionist to the point where he gets so absorbed in something that time and people cease to exist—but…I love him. We're still young, we've probably got another twenty or thirty years together, if fate is kind, and we both know we want to spend that time together.'

'I can't believe it.' Jessica gave her mother a big hug, and then sat back to gaze into her face. 'I just can't believe it.'

'You're happy for us, then?' her mother asked anxiously.

'Ecstatic.'

'We were going to tell you and Jo later, once he was home, but I've told you tonight because I want you to understand that real love is worth enduring anything for,' her mother said urgently. 'I shouldn't have left him; I knew it within months of leaving, but it was too late then—things had been said and everything was so bitter and final. But we never stopped loving each other,' she finished sadly. 'So give your Colt a chance, Jessica, and then another one, and another one, until he comes through.'

They talked some more in the peace and tranquillity of the little garden, finding strength from each other, and although Jessica's heart was still sore and bruised on the ride home through the dark streets the warmth of her mother's love stayed with her.

What was she going to do now? she asked herself as the taxi neared home. She had burnt her bridges with Russell—she really couldn't see him welcoming her back after the exhibition she had made of herself that evening—so it looked as though job hunting was definitely on the agenda.

But it wasn't her career or her financial status that was gnawing away at her. She loved Colt. She would always love him. She couldn't bear to think that she would have to spend the rest of her life without him.

None of that, she told herself tightly as she felt the tears begin to prick at the back of her eyes. She'd cried enough for one evening, and all the tears in the world wouldn't change anything.

After paying the taxi driver she stood for a moment in the deserted street, the sky a black canopy overhead dotted with a myriad twinkling stars and the city air warm and still. Somewhere in the distance a dog barked, the sound lonely and mournful in the quietness, and again she felt tears prick at her eyes. What was he doing now? Was he thinking of her? And, if so, were they thoughts of hate, annoyance, or merely irritation that she had popped up in his life again? Or—she bit on her lip as the thought seared her mind—had he other things on his mind? Black-haired, blue-eyed, voluptuous things?

She turned abruptly, opening the door with a savage little twist of the key and closing it behind her before running quickly up the stairs without bothering to turn on the light, her heart desperately sore. How could you hate someone and love them in the same breath?

As she reached the landing, her heart gave an excruciatingly hard hammer-blow against her ribcage as a dark shadow loomed up from the floor, causing her to freeze with fright.

'Jessica?' She almost fainted with relief when she recognised Colt's voice. 'Where the hell have you been?' he growled furiously.

CHAPTER ELEVEN

'WHERE have I been?' Jessica's relief was ousted by a mixture of emotions—fear at what he was going to say to her after the scene that night, anger at his presumptuous tone, shame that just the sound of his voice had the power to make her dizzy... 'What's it to you where I've been?' she asked tightly.

'*Jessica*—' He stopped abruptly, his growl mellowing as she switched on the light on the side of the wall and he saw her swollen eyes. 'I was worried about you,' he said gruffly. She said nothing, her hand at her mouth as she surveyed his handsome, unreadable features, watching him quietly as he brushed his trousers, which were gritty from the floor. 'Your friend downstairs let me in,' he said softly. 'I've been waiting for you.'

'Have you?' Her heart was beating so loudly, the sound was reverberating in her ears. 'Why?'

'To tell you you've won,' he said simply. He was standing quite still now, his powerful, muscled body appearing even larger on the small landing and his dark face like stone, only his eyes seeming alive.

'Won?' She stared at him uncomprehendingly, her body as still as his. 'Won what?'

'My heart, such as it is. You're worth more, much more than that, I know. But for what it's worth you have my heart; you had it from the first moment we met.'

'Colt...' She felt her grip on reality fading fast. 'Don't...don't play with me.'

'*Play with you?*' The control slipped for a moment and then was held, but as he went to reach out to her she shrank back against the wall, her eyes enormous in the whiteness of her face. 'Hell, Jessica, is that what you think I'm doing?'

'Where is she?' She forced the words out through numb lips, her mind caught in a maelstrom of whirling confusion. He hadn't been near her for days, he had taken that…that creature to the party, and now he was here telling her he cared for her?

'Who?' And then he understood, his voice softening as he said, 'Veronica? Safely tucked up in bed with her husband, I should imagine. I looked for you after your…précis of my character, to introduce you to him, but you'd gone.'

'Her husband?' Oh, no, no, she hadn't made the worst blunder in the world, had she? She couldn't have; it had been so *obvious*…

'I didn't take Veronica to the reception, Jessica,' Colt said gently. 'I didn't take anyone, as it happens, but Veronica and her husband were in my party.'

'But she…she was all over you,' Jessica said bewilderedly.

'Veronica is all over any man with a healthy bank balance,' Colt said grimly. 'Except her husband, who unfortunately is a friend of mine—which necessitates enduring his wife's company with politeness, if nothing else.'

'I wasn't polite,' she whispered, horror-stricken.

'That you weren't.' A shadow of a smile touched the hard mouth. 'But she'd had that coming a long, long time, and you were right, Jessica. Veronica is the sort of woman I deserve. But…but I don't want what I deserve—I haven't wanted it since the first moment I laid eyes on you, but I didn't have the guts to admit it to myself,' he said bleakly.

'Colt—'

'I've been more miserable in the last few days than in the rest of my life put together,' he said painfully. 'And still I didn't have the guts to get down on my knees and thank you for loving me. The money, the power, it was like dross—tainted, without you. But I was scared, scared stiff. And then tonight I saw I'd hurt you; I faced the fact that I'd probably driven you away... Have I? Have I driven you away, Jessica? I'm sorry, so sorry, my love.' His voice was anguished but he didn't reach for her again. She saw his face was naked for her to read, and what she read was love.

'Colt...' She knew her legs were going to give way, but in the next second he had gathered her up in his arms, raining kisses over her face and her throat as he cradled her against him.

'I love you, Jessica; you're everything I've ever wanted—believe that. If it takes the rest of my life I'll prove it to you...' She could barely understand his incoherent murmuring as he punctuated the words with burning kisses which were bemusing, bewitching. And for long moments she clung to him as they touched and tasted and loved, before she struggled away, the movement instantly making his eyes wary and watchful with a dark fear that she understood now. He feared rejection, just like the rest of the human race.

'Inside; we'd better go inside,' she whispered weakly, opening the door and stepping into her tiny bedsit before turning to face him again. 'Colt, love is scary,' she said softly, her hand reaching out to touch the severe line of his mouth as he continued to watch her. 'But I'd rather be scared with you than without you. I love you, I know I'll always love you, but I'm not making you give anything you can't give. I'll be yours as long as you want me—'

He cut off her words with his lips, taking her mouth in a passionate kiss of intense hunger that sent them both up in flames. His tongue parted her lips, sending bolts of pleasure into every nerve in her body as he tasted the sweetness within, holding her so close she could feel the thunderous pounding of his heart against the wall of his chest and the thrusting evidence of his manhood against her softness.

There was molten fire flowing where her blood had been, consuming all the pain and heartache of the last few weeks in a river of tumultuous joy. She didn't care about tomorrow, the future—he was here now, loving her, and that was enough.

As their lovemaking spiralled she felt herself melting with the longing to become one, but as her hands feverishly fumbled with his trousers, his jacket long since discarded, she felt his hands on hers. 'No, not now, not yet.'

'What?' She raised herself from where they were lying on the sofa, her fingers moving to the hard planes of his chest covered in dark, curling body hair that his unbuttoned shirt revealed, its texture silky against her skin. 'What's wrong?' she asked softly, her face suddenly anxious.

'Nothing's wrong, but not now, my love.' He reached for his jacket, extracting an envelope and handing it to her. 'Will you marry me, Jessica? Live with me, love me, bear...bear my children?' His voice had caught on the last words and she knew he was thinking of that other little being Netta had taken from him, the child he had lost along with the rest of his family.

'Marry you?' She stared at the special licence in her hand. 'But...when...?'

'A couple of days ago.' He answered the question with a wry smile. 'I got it a couple of days ago. I've been in torment, Jessica; I haven't been able to think straight, to sleep, but I knew I had to make you see you weren't like the others. From the first moment I saw you I knew that, but we got off to such a bad start.'

'But a marvellous finish,' she said tearfully, her heart bursting with love for this cold, warm, complex, simple man.

'I love you, Jessica. There'll never be anyone but you, and I want this done right,' he said softly. 'So, will you marry me, tomorrow? Will you live with me and be my love?'

'Yes, yes, yes, yes…' And he caught the words, savouring them as he sealed the vow with a kiss.

'Carol will never forgive me, you know.' Jessica stretched carefully, like a sleek, satisfied, well-fed cat, running one hand over the dark, muscled contours of Colt's stomach as she admired the plain gold band on the third finger of her left hand. 'We'd always promised each other we could be bridesmaids at each other's wedding, and here's me not even having told her I'm married.'

'They'll all have the telegrams by now,' Colt said lazily, as though that made everything all right. 'I've promised everyone a big party when we get back.'

'She still won't like it,'' Jessica warned. 'Us sneaking away like this.'

'We haven't sneaked anywhere.' Colt raised himself on one elbow, looking at her with those devastating grey eyes that glowed as they took in the smooth outline of her flesh under the minuscule bikini. They had been married three whole days and nights—glorious, wonderful nights, when she had been awakened to things she had never dreamt of even in the most erotic of her dreams. After one night at a London hotel they had flown out to the Caribbean, where Jessica felt as though she had stepped into another world, a world of waving palm trees, brilliant blue skies, white beaches and azure seas.

'And there's hardly any point in wearing that thing.' He flicked at the tiny pants before moving over her, peeling the tiny flaps of the bikini top from her full breasts before taking each rosy peak in turn.

She ought to protest, Jessica thought dazedly, lost in the pleasure of what he was doing to her. Although the large garden of their luxurious villa was quite private, there were the maids…

'They've gone to the market.' He read her thoughts, as always. 'To buy some oysters for dinner to keep my strength up,' he added wickedly as he eased her thighs up, removing the pants and dropping them to the floor along with his own trunks.

Keep his strength up? Jessica thought, shivering with ecstasy as his mouth moved over her moistness. She had lost count of the number of times he had made love to her—and she knew it was love, his tenderness unquestionable even in the deepest throes of passion, his devotion absolute.

'You know, you were right.' He stopped for a moment, relaxing back on the huge double sun-lounger as his eyes stroked over her body laid out before him. 'Dead right.'

'About what?' she asked throatily, reaching up for him, her body aching for the pleasure only he could give.

'Satisfaction was guaranteed,' he said softly, his breath catching in his throat as her fingers paid homage to his masculinity. 'And well worth waiting for.'

And then there were just the sounds of love in the scented warmth of the sheltered garden, the deep blue of the swimming pool at their side reflecting the sapphire sky overhead as their bodies came together in a blaze of ecstasy that took them to the heights and beyond.

MILLS & BOON®

Next Month's Romances

♡

Each month you can choose from a wide variety of romance novels from Mills & Boon. Below are the new titles to look out for next month from the Presents™ and Enchanted™ series.

Presents™

PERFECT MARRIAGE MATERIAL	Penny Jordan
LOVESTRUCK	Charlotte Lamb
A MARRIAGE TO REMEMBER	Carole Mortimer
A VERY PUBLIC AFFAIR	Sally Wentworth
RECKLESS ENGAGEMENT	Daphne Clair
CHRISTMAS WITH A STRANGER	Catherine Spencer
A FRAGILE MARRIAGE	Rosalie Ash
THE GROOM'S REVENGE	Kate Walker

Enchanted™

THE COURTING CAMPAIGN	Catherine George
TEMPORARY HUSBAND	Day Leclaire
NO WIFE REQUIRED!	Rebecca Winters
BABY IN THE BOARDROOM	Rosemary Gibson
DO YOU TAKE THIS COWBOY?	Jeanne Allan
KISSED BY A STRANGER	Valerie Parv
RAINY DAY KISSES	Debbie Macomber
EXPECTATIONS	Shannon Waverly

Available from WH Smith, John Menzies, Volume One, Forbuoys, Martins, Tesco, Asda, Safeway and other paperback stockists.

MISSING LINKS

How would you like to win a year's supply of Mills & Boon® books? Well you can and they're FREE! Simply complete the competition below and send it to us by 30th April 1998. The first five correct entries picked after the closing date will each win a year's subscription to the Mills & Boon series of their choice. What could be easier?

1. APPLE	P I E	CRUST
2. STRAWBERRY	_ _ _	TARTS
3. MINCED	_ _ _ _	BALLS
4. PICKLED	_ _ _ _ _	RING
5. GRAPE	_ _ _ _ _	JUICE
6. FRENCH	_ _ _ _ _	SAUCE
7. TOFFEE	_ _ _ _ _	CRUMBLE
8. PEANUT	_ _ _ _ _ _	BEANS
9. TANDOORI	_ _ _ _ _ _ _	CURRY
10. PRAWN	_ _ _ _ _ _ _ _	SAUSAGES

C7J

Please turn over for details of how to enter ⇨

HOW TO ENTER

There are ten missing words in our list overleaf. Each of
the missing words must link up with the two words on
either side to make a type of food.

For example, the word *Pie* links with *Apple* and
Crust to form *Apple Pie* and *Pie Crust*:
APPLE - PIE - CRUST

As you find each one, write it in the space provided,
we've done the first one for you! When you have linked
up all the words, don't forget to fill in the coupon below,
pop this page in an envelope and post it today—you
don't even need a stamp!
Hurry, competition ends 30th April 1998.

Mills & Boon® Missing Links Competition
FREEPOST, Croydon, Surrey, CR9 3WZ

EIRE readers send competition to PO Box 4546, Dublin 24.

Please tick the series you would like to receive
if you are a winner:

Presents™ ❏ Enchanted™ ❏ Medical Romance™ ❏
Historical Romance™ ❏ Temptation® ❏

Are you a Reader Service™ Subscriber?   Yes ❏   No ❏

Ms/Mrs/Miss/Mr _____
                                              (BLOCK CAPS PLEASE)
Address_____

_____

_____ Postcode_____

(I am over 18 years of age)   C7J
One application per household. Competition open to residents of the
UK and Ireland only. You may be mailed with offers from other
reputable companies as a result of this application. If you would prefer
not to receive such offers, please tick box. ❏

Mills & Boon is a registered trademark of
Harlequin Mills & Boon Limited.

MILLS & BOON®

Christmas Treats

A sparkling new anthology
—the perfect Christmas gift!

Celebrate the season with a taste of love in this delightful collection of brand-new short stories combining the pleasures of food and love.

Figgy Pudding
by PENNY JORDAN
All the Trimmings
by LINDSAY ARMSTRONG
A Man For All Seasonings
by DAY LECLAIRE

And, as an extra treat, we've included the authors' own recipe ideas in this collection—because no yuletide would be complete without...Christmas Dinner!

Get swept away by

RISING
Tides

by award-winning author EMILIE RICHARDS

The reading of a woman's will threatens to destroy her family.

In this explosive sequel to the critically acclaimed Iron Lace, family, friends and strangers gather for the reading of Aurore Gerritsen's will. The threat of an approaching hurricane becomes a minor incident as each bequest reveals yet another dark family secret.

Valid only in the UK & Ireland against purchases made in retail outlets and not in conjunction with any Reader Service or other offer.

50ᵖ OFF
COUPON

VALID UNTIL: 31.1.1998

EMILIE RICHARDS' *RISING TIDES*

9 904170 190503 >

0472 00172